Hotchkiss' Handbook to
HUMMEL
ART
With Current Prices

Courtesy Ars Edition.

Hotchkiss' Handbook to
HUMMEL ART
With Current Prices

Copyright © 1982,
John F. Hotchkiss, Trustee
ISBN 0-87069-421-9

10 9 8 7 6 5 4 3 2 1

Art Director, Jann Williams
Editors, Liz Fletcher,
    Ginger Van Blaricom
Typesetting by Typeco, Inc.
Printed by Walsworth
    Publishing Co.,
    Marceline, Missouri
Color by Art Lithocraft,
    Kansas City, Missouri

Published by

Wallace-Homestead Book Company
1912 Grand Avenue
Des Moines, Iowa 50305

Contents

Acknowledgments

To the hundreds of contributors who have generously shared their special knowledge of Hummel Art, my grateful appreciation. In particular, Dorothy Dous, director of the Hummel Collectors' Club and Joan Ostroff, vice-president of the Goebel Collectors' Club deserve special mention for their close cooperation and excellent suggestions which have helped to make *Hotchkiss' Handbook to Hummel Art* easy to use and accurately informative.

Introduction

This unique, four-color Handbook has been written to provide collectors with quick, accurate answers to questions about genuine Hummel Art in both two- and three-dimensional forms. It is a buyer's, seller's, dealer's and appraiser's condensed, pocket or purse version of our major reference book *Hummel Art II*. It includes all of the latest developments in M.J.Hummel ceramics by Goebel and, for the first time, extensive information about the new lines of Hummel graphics and accessories distributed by Ars Edition, Inc., owner of more than three hundred original drawings created by Sister Hummel. Beginning collectors will find essential information about buying hundreds of articles of Hummel Art, with prices that range from less than ten dollars to over ten thousand dollars in value. Some examples are less than a month old and some are almost fifty years old.

For the advanced collectors, this book updates what they already know and puts in their pocket and purse a compact listing of the M.J.Hummel Collection with more than 4,000 current prices, which includes the recent introductions as well as the deletions. Some of these models will never be made again. Readers will also find cross-references to *Hummel Art II* for detailed information and advice on such subjects as repairs, reproductions, care, and insurance of their collections of Hummel Art derived from the drawings that Sister Maria Innocentia Hummel created in the twelve short years prior to her untimely death in 1946.

How to Use This Book

This book contains more information, prices, and four-color photographs than any other Hummel book in print. All of the information about each M.J.Hummel model has been consolidated on one page of this book. The figurines and other articles are presented in the numerical order which matches the production numbers incised on the bottom of each piece produced by Goebel. Under that number you will find the correct name of the piece, its photograph, sizes, trademarks showing the current values of each known variation, and a concise history containing vital collecting information.

If you know only the name of the figurine, refer to the Alphabetical Index on page 158 to find its number. If you know neither the number or the name study the photograph until you find the one you want. If you can't locate it, it is probably not a genuine M.J.Hummel figurine, but see page 8 to be sure.

Information about Sister M.I. Hummel's original drawings, signatures,

Print H 349 published by Ars Edition from one of the original Hummel drawings in their collection.

Little Nurse, reproduction of original drawing, H 455 from Ars Edition.

376 Little Nurse, *issued 1982, TMK-6, courtesy Goebel Collectors' Club.*

A photograph of Sister Maria Innocentia and an example of how she signed most of her world-famous art. Courtesy Ars Sacra.

Serious conference between Sister Maria Innocentia and several of her students photographed in the early Thirties. Girl with bow in her bobbed hair and thoughtful little boy bear a striking resemblance to a number of M. I. Hummel figurines.

values, and graphics produced by Ars Edition in various forms can be found beginning on page 5. These have been reproduced from over three hundred original Hummel drawings that are owned by Ars Sacra, parent company of Ars Edition, Inc. Ars Sacra purchased and published the first reproduction of their Hummel drawings in 1934. The very first Hummel figurines, released in 1935, were sculpted by Goebel craftsmen using Ars Sacra postcards as models.

To appreciate the scope of Sister Hummel's creations, allow some time to go through the whole book page by page even though it is a superficial perusal the first time. And remember, in any field of art and collecting, the best informed person will always be the most successful collector.

Hummel Art II

For a complete reference work on this subject, you will find *Hummel Art II* invaluable as it covers what is in this handbook in greater detail, plus the following essential subjects and color illustrations that are not included herein such as a more detailed biography of Sister Hummel's life and more pictures and suggestions on how to recognize her original drawings. A chapter of important variations priced in this book are shown for identification. Photographs and advice on how to distinguish genuine M.I. Hummel products by the Goebel Company from the large number of reproductions are featured, plus charts, pictures and comments on how figurines have been marked and manufactured since 1935.

M.I. Hummel dolls, calendars, Schmid productions derived from her pre-convent years, needlework kits, and other Hummel art forms such as Dubler, Beswick, Arnart, and Napco Hummel and Hummel-like figurines are covered in depth.

The sections of where to buy and sell figurines, insuring and protecting them are especially timely. Complete instructions on how to appraise your own collection that will be accepted by most insurance companies are given, as well as the type to buy to protect against theft and especially breakage.

The names of many national dealers, clubs, exhibits, festivals, seminars, and contests are listed with the addresses. (Memberships in the Hummel Collectors' Club and the Goebel Collectors' Club afford especially valuable opportunities of keeping current in this fast-moving hobby.)

Repairing, cleaning, safeguarding, displaying, and photographing figurines are other helpful subjects. These are described and illustrated in detail with addresses of the sources of supply.

If you don't have a copy of the deluxe, hardcover book of 260 pages and over 500 pieces in color, one can be obtained from your bookstore, gift shop, or department store.

Sister Maria Innocentia Hummel

Sister Hummel was christened Berta shortly after her birth on May 21, 1909, in Massing, Lower Bavaria. Not too many years later her father was called away to serve in the German army before World War I. Her artistic talent was evident in her early school years and she illustrated many letters and cards to her father during his army service. She was an active, perhaps precocious, child, on the go arranging plays, dressing up in grown-ups' clothes, and always to be found where the action was. She made good use of any scrap of paper she could find to record quick, impetuous sketches of incidents she observed, usually with her own subtle humor or exaggeration added for impact. Even before she acquired formal training in art, her friends and classmates were continually imploring her to "Sketch me, Berta."

In her teens she was admitted to the prestigious Academy of Applied Arts in Munich, where her artistic skills developed by leaps and bounds, and teachers quickly realized her great potential. During these years she became acquainted with two nuns who were also attending the academy. It is possible this association may have influenced her in her religious vocation. After completing her work at the academy she elected to enter the Franciscan Convent in Siessen in 1931 rather than to continue advanced study in art. She took her first vows in 1933 and, while still a postulant, found time to create many light-hearted drawings of the young children she loved so much in addition to more seriously rendered religious subjects.

In August of 1933, the convent submitted samples of her sketches to the firm of Joseph Müller, Verlag Ars Sacra in Munich to see if they would be interested in publishing her work. Her drawings were quickly accepted. The postcards and prints made from these were in such great demand, she was continually entreated to send new ones. A contract ensued which gave the Joseph Müller firm exclusive ownership and rights to more than three-hundred drawings, many of them inspired by suggestions from Mrs. Müller.

At the convent Sister Hummel was the "busy bee" that her name implies in German. She taught art to young students, designed religious garments, and created a number of murals in addition to producing a stream of drawings for her publishing firm. A museum at the Siessen Convent now houses some of her published and unpublished works. The only sculpture she ever made is one of the prized exhibits and is named the Infant of Krumbad.

In the late 1930s, Sister Hummel developed a respiratory ailment, but did not slow the pace and diligence she applied to her art and her religious commitments. She continued as long as she was able to create her lovable pastel drawings of children. Finally, her health seriously declined, and she was admitted to a sanitarium with acute tuberculosis. Perhaps the zeal with which she accomplished so much was prompted by a premonition that the time remaining to her was to be tragically brief.

After several treatments in sanitariums Sister Maria Innocentia Hummel returned to her beloved convent in October, 1946, and passed away one month later, leaving behind her the priceless heritage which millions now treasure as Hummel Art.

Original Hummel Art

Original Hummel Art refers to any sketches, drawings, and paintings that were created by Berta, later to be known as Sister Maria Innocentia Hummel, during her lifetime. Most of the art that she produced before she entered the convent is now controlled by the Hummel family in Massing. The art she created during her convent years is controlled by the convent, with few exceptions.

The most comprehensive exhibition of her work produced before she became a nun was organized by Paul Schmid III, president of Schmid Brothers, Inc., Randolph, Maryland. It was his uncle, John Schmid, who imported the first Hummel figurines into the U.S. in 1935. This exhibit traveled throughout the country during 1981 and early 1982. A catalog of the exhibition remains as an excellent record of some of her untutored work as well as some of her advanced studies in oils, water colors, and pastels. Many were unsigned, but one fine oil painting of her parish church in Massing was signed B. Hummel, '29. Others were signed with either the initials "B.H." in block letters or merely the letter H. One was signed Berta Hummel and one, ~~Hummel~~ in her highly individualistic style. Until 1931 it is doubtful if any quantity of it was sold, but certainly there are examples of

"The River Rott in Massing," 1929, oil, 17½" by 13". Described as "the most mature and professional artistic statement of Berta Hummel's pre-convent years." The parish church that Berta attended is in the background.

"Hungarian Girl," 1928, watercolor, 10½" by 7", subject costumed in the manner of gypsies who roamed Central Europe during Berta's childhood.

Reproduction of original Sister Hummel drawing available from Ars Edition as H 204.

M.I. Hummel figurine made from the sculpture created by Gerhard Skrobek in 1957. Issued by Goebel as Ring Around the Rosie, Hum. 348.

many sketches she made of her friends and schoolmates.

During her convent days she worked mostly in pastels because she could get her ideas down on paper faster as she worked impetuously, the amount of detail sometimes depending on the time available to put her concepts on paper. Dr. Elizabeth Dubler, onetime director of Joseph Müller, Verlag Ars Sacra, once told the author that she could almost sense Sister's emotional state from the way the drawing was executed. Most of these drawings are signed with the simple script signature, *Hummel* .

Over three hundred of the drawings she drew while in the convent are owned by Joseph Müller, Verlag Ars Sacra of Munich and their recently established company in the U.S., Ars Edition, Inc. of Seaford, New York. Ars Edition is continuously arranging exhibits of limited numbers of some of her very famous drawings in this country and may in the future establish a permanent home for them here in a special museum. Most of these works owned by her first publisher were merely signed *Hummel* . A number of her religious subjects are signed *M.J. Hummel* , the use of which on any derivative of her originals is the provenance of the Goebel Company through arrangements with the Franciscan Convent in Siessen.

Other originals by her hand are owned by the Goebel Company. The convent has now set up a special museum of the ones they have, plus her only known sculpture. There are some original drawings in the Robert and Ruth Miller Collection and in other private hands both here and in Germany. Some were done as personal favors by Sister. Infrequently, one of these is available for purchase. The author is aware of about six that have been offered for sale in the last four years. These are likely to have fetched between four to ten thousand dollars.

Sister Hummel is known to have made duplicate originals of some drawings, and they are so marked on the back. It has also been reported that a number of fakes of her work were produced in the 1950s after her art became so popular with G.I.'s from this country. In fact a painting of one of her well-known motifs was sent to this author with the claim that it was one of her originals. This copy was done in oils, while the original was done in pastels and its location is known. Those collectors interested in owning an original by her should not depend on the signature or their judgment alone. Expert opinion is available from several sources. Furthermore, the fine large lithographic prints that can be matted and framed at a very modest sum could make it unnecessary to incur such risks.

Derivatives of Original Hummel Art

Because of the widespread attachment of millions to the work of Sister Hummel, the number and forms of adaptations of her originals are constantly increasing, some from previously unknown work and others from well-known ones in different forms.

Without doubt the greatest variety and quantities of articles that have been officially reproduced are in the form of graphics by her two publishers. For almost fifty years, they have faithfully reproduced lithographs in original color and detail from the originals. Most of these have been licensed by the Franciscan Convent of which she was a member. They have been made in a range of sizes from small prints and postcards, to large, 20″ and 26″ sizes suitable for framing. A number of books of her drawings, supplemented with related poems, and also annual calendars, have been published in Germany. Most of this work has been published by Joseph Müller, Verlag Ars Sacra in

Munich and its new company in the U.S., Ars Edition, Inc. They own over three hundred of her original works, many of which were done as commissions, in the early 1930s. Emil Fink Verlag of Stuttgart is another publishing house that has produced graphics from a more limited line of originals.

Schmid Brothers, Inc., of Randolph, Maryland, has issued a number of varied designs of her work made before she entered the convent. These items include graphics, limited edition plates, bells, paperweights, plaques, and many articles utilizing her work as decoupage decorations. For a detailed listing and color illustrations of Schmid's products see *Hummel Art II*.

The Goebel Company of Rodental, West Germany, is the only authorized producer of adaptation of Sister Hummel's drawings in three-dimensional, ceramic form.

They have an exclusive contract with Franciscan Convent in Siessen and a royalty agreement which has paid the convent millions of dollars since 1935. The contract provides that the convent (originally Sister Hummel) must approve each adaptation of any of her drawings before the adaptation can be manufactured for sale. Products cannot be incised with her facsimile signature without the convent's express approval.

Other three-dimensional figurines have been produced in the past by Beswick of England and a Dubler Company in the U.S. These were made during WW II years when the supply from Germany was cut off. These are marked "Hummel" or "M.I. Hummel." The authenticity and licensing of these has never been established, and from their appearance and quality it is highly unlikely that they would have continued being made once Goebel started producing again in 1946.

Naturally with any art as heartwarming and widely accepted as that of Sister Hummel, many unauthorized copies or fakes have been made. Sometimes they are called "Hummel Look-Alikes." Currently Napco and Arnart, both New York importers, have extensive lines known as "Our Children" and "Original Child Life Series" respectively. These are, for the most part, being produced in Japan. Many others without any identification have been found. All of the reproductions have been illustrated, described, and priced in detail in Chapter 5 of *Hummel Art II*.

Collecting Hummel Art

Worldwide, hundreds of thousands of people have collections of some form of Hummel Art (using the definition that one piece is a sample, two is a pair, and three or more is a collection). Some have been purchased by the owner; some received as gifts or bequests. Many G.I.'s brought M.I. Hummel figurines from Germany after WWII, an action which stimulated a huge demand for Hummel Art in all forms in the American market. Now, M.J. Hummel figurines can be purchased in more than 10,000 stores in this country alone, and there are hundreds of official dealers in Germany and other countries.

One sage said that before you start to collect, read a good book on the subject. This is especially good advice if you intend to buy Hummel Art at flea markets, auctions, garage sales, and tag sales. Readers' letters have proved conclusively that the best informed collectors make the best buys and are enjoying their collections more because they know the background and varied histories of each piece. While a complete book could be (and has) been written on this subject alone, it is suggested that you buy *new* Hummel Art of any description from an authorized and reputable dealer. But be aware that a few outlets may charge more than the suggested retail price, as some airport shops

Whitsuntide, Hum. 163 with Incised Crown, TMK-1 and incised 163 (model number); printed black Germany. Also Full Bee, TMK-2 in black. Rare.

TMK-1
CROWN MARK

1935-1942

1A Single Incised Crown
1B Single Stamped Crown
1C Double Incised Crown
1D Incised & Stamped Crown
1E Incised Crown plus Full
    Bee Stamped.

1A   1B
1935-1942

―――――

TMK-2
FULL BEE MARK

1950-1958

2A Incised Full Bee
2B Stamped Full Bee
    (black or blue)
2C Stamped Small Bee
2D Stamped High Bee
2E Stamped Low Bee

Dates and designs are approximate.

2A   2B
1950-1958

2C   2D   2E
1956   1957   1958

TMK-3
STYLIZED BEE MARK

1956-1960

3A   Early Partial Stylized Bee,
     Stamped
3B   Large Stylized Bee,
     Incised Circle
3C   Large Stamped Stylized Bee,
     W. Germany
3D   Small Stylized Transfer Bee,
     W. Germany

3A   3B
1958   1956-1960

W. Germany
3C
1960-1969

W. Germany
3D
1960-1972

TMK-4
THREE LINE MARK

© by
W. Goebel
W. Germany
1963-1972
4A   Small Stylized Bee,
Blue Transfer Underglaze

Dates and designs are approximate.

do, and offer no knowledge to guide or assist the collector. If you have read this book, and through personal experience and guidance have acquired a good working knowledge of Hummel Art, you are qualified to buy in the secondary markets mentioned previously. These markets are an important source of interesting variations, discontinued items not available in most shops, or just plain "sleepers" (underpriced) that will add zest to your collecting.

One of the best ways of keeping continually informed is provided by membership in both of the national clubs formed over five years ago for M.J.Hummel figurine collectors. Send a request to the Hummel Collectors' Club, P.O. Box 257, Yardley, PA 19067, for a sample copy of its newsletter. The club publishes four issues a year which, in addition to keeping you current on Hummel figurines and events, contain a popular section devoted to the buying or selling of Hummel figurines among club members. (If you wish, Dorothy Dous, the editor will act as intermediary in such transactions.)

The Goebel Collector's Club is located in a beautiful converted mansion at 105 White Plains Road, Tarrytown, NY 10591, that includes a museum of old and new Goebel products, with particular emphasis on Hummels. The club's *Insights* magazine is published four times a year. It contains educational articles, news about new issues and deletions, and locations and dates of special promotions. There is a readers' page where questions are answered. Each year members of the club are issued redemption cards that entitle them to buy a special, limited edition M.J.Hummel item available to club members only, through authorized dealers.

Those interested in graphics and accessories can get on the Ars Edition mailing list for their new catalogs. This will keep you up to date on what is new in genuine Hummel graphics and collectibles. Write to: Ars Edition, Inc., 3876 Merrick Rd., Seaford, NY 11783.

Most Hummel collectors have insatiable appetites for information about their hobby and supplementary services. Topics such as where or how to repair damaged figures; locations of forums, festivals, and local clubs; how to buy and sell a collection; and safeguarding and insuring prized items of Hummel art are of concern. These examples and other topics of interest an information such as how to appraise and insure your own collection will be found in our standard reference book, *Hummel Art II.* There are also about twenty pages of helpful instructions, suggestions, and names and addresses of suppliers provided to make the collecting of Hummel Art fun and even profitable.

Collecting M.I. Hummel Figurines

The most frequently asked question in the thousand or more letters we have received in the mail is whether or not the piece in question is a genuine M.J.Hummel piece. Most of the time we can give a fairly positive yes or no, especially if a good photograph is submitted. Recognizing this need we have developed a short checklist that any reader can use to determine authenticity for themselves. The most important feature to check is No. 1. It is preeminent.

1. Is the article incised (indented) with the facsimile of Sister Hummel's actual signature that looks like this? M.J.Hummel
2. Does the shape, color, model number, and illustration match the same model number in this book?
3. Does it have a trademark that looks like one of the six shown on page 9?

Mark/ First Used	Trademark	Mark/ First Used
TMK-1 (Crown) 1935		TMK-4 (Three Line) 1964
TMK-2 (Full Bee) 1950		TMK-5 (Goebel Bee) 1972
TMK-3 (Stylized) 1957		TMK-6 (Current) 1979

4. Do some other marks shown in the M.I. Hummel Pedigree chart on page 11 appear on the piece in question?

The trademark identifies it *only* as a Goebel product, *not a Hummel*. All Goebel products carry a trademark, but only Hummels bear the incised facsimile signature M.J.Hümmel. The so-called "Bee" marks confuse some collectors since "hummel" in German means bumblebee. The presence of the Goebel trademark does not prove that the article so marked is a Hummel.

Exceptions to the above statements exist but they are few. For example, if there is no model number but the M.J.Hümmel is incised, it is genuine. Some collectors are unwilling to pay full price for such a piece. From 1946 to 1948 Goebel was required to stamp each piece "Made in U.S. Zone." Some of these do not carry a Goebel trademark but are incised M.J.Hümmel.

The primary purpose of the Goebel trademarks was just discussed and their intended purpose was to identify the company of origin (Goebel). But to collectors they have a second important significance. Each trademark indicates the approximate span of years during which the piece was made and therefore is a major factor in determining the price. The earlier the trademark, the more valuable the piece. The Crown mark, TMK-1, was first used in 1935. Please note that a complete resume of all of these marks are shown on the margins of these pages along with most of the variations and approximate dates they were used. They deserve careful study and memorizing.

When the current TMK-6 was introduced in 1979, another change of importance to collectors was made. The artists who paint the faces were then permitted to place an identifying brushmark on the bottom of the base. Some of these were in the form of the artist's initials or other symbols. Also, beginning in 1979, the artist added the year date in which the face was painted. This is shown as the last two years of the century, i.e, '79, and is clearly illustrated on the M.I. Hummel Pedigree, page 11, Hum. 112/I, in the lower right portion.

Model Numbers and Size Indicators

It was mentioned earlier that the model number incised on an example should match the picture and table appearing alongside that same number in this book. All model numbers from 1 to 400 are accounted for, and some beyond 400. A few numbers have no pictures. These are ones for which a sample has not yet been located or which the company has cancelled prior to production. Other model numbers are illustrated with a reproduction of a drawing by Sister Hummel indicating the theme of the future figurine.

TMK-5 GOEBEL-BEE

1972-1979

5A Blue Transfer, Underglaze
5B Blue Transfer, Overglaze
5C Blue Transfer, Overglaze, Hand-dated, 1979

TMK-6 GOEBEL ONLY

Goebel
W.Germany

1979- ?

6A Blue Transfer, Overglaze
6B Blue Transfer, Overglaze, Hand-dated

Additional Identification Used with Some of the Above Trademarks

Stamped "U.S. Zone" used with TMK 1 in 1947 and 1948.

Made in U.S. Zone	U.S. Zone

U.S. Zone

Germany

Stamped "W. Goebel" used sometimes randomly with copyright year in the 1950s and 1960s.

© W. GOEBEL

Incised Production Control number are two small, incised random numerals.

R (for registered) stamped next to some early TMK-2, Full Bee marks.

© (for copyrighted) stamped or incised along with incised copyright year on some.

Small painted artist initial or mark. Starting in 1979 the two digit year was added.

Dates and designs are approximate.

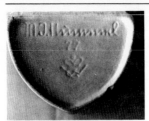

TMK-1A, Incised Crown with incised M.I. Hummel signature and model number 77. On base of Cross with Doves Font. Extremely rare example. Photograph courtesy Cheryl Trotter.

TMK-1, base of Globe Trotter, Hum. 79, without Crown mark; stamped US Zone and Germany; no copyright date.

TMK-1, Incised Crown and model number 58/0 on base of Playmates. Stamped U.S.-Zone (over) Germany. No year date.

When a new model or motif is put into production, a master mold is made which determines the approximate height of the finished piece and a model number is incised. Later on Goebel may decide to make that same model available in another size, either larger or smaller. To eliminate confusion and to distinguish one size from another, Goebel has added what is termed an indicator mark for each different size in any one model. This is done by following the model number with a diagonal slash mark (/), and then another number. If the new size is smaller than the original model, the whole number will usually be followed by /0. If another still smaller size is added to the line the indicator would be /2/0. When the new size is larger than the original whole number size, the model number is followed by /I (Roman numeral one) and so on, as the sizes get larger. Taking the Little Hiker as an example, it was first assigned model number 16, $5\frac{1}{2}''$ tall. Later, this was replaced with two other sizes. The smaller $4\frac{1}{2}''$ size is designated in catalogs and incised on the bottom 16/2/0. The larger size was about 6'' tall when it was issued and was designated as 16/I. Sometime in the 1950s a still smaller size was issued that was only 4'' tall which was designated as 16/3/0. Check the "Indicator" column for Little Hiker on p. 19 where this model-size production is shown.

There are several variations in model number designations that are not fully understood. One is the use of the arabic numerals instead of the Roman ones. For example, the Little Hiker that is 6'' high has been found incised 16/I (Roman) and 16/1 (arabic). Another unexplained variation is the use of the decimal point after a model number. Little Hiker, $5\frac{1}{2}''$ high, which is normally incised 16 on the bottom of the base, is also found with 16. (decimal after the whole number). The ones that are marked in arabic size indicators or whole numbers followed by the decimal are considered more interesting than the conventional ones to collectors. There appear to be fewer of these two variations, and the ones with arabic numerals or decimal points tend to bring a premium when sold. The premium varies because some model numbers have many of these variations. School Girl, 81. (decimal), is one that comes to mind. So premiums are a matter of choice, but may be from 10 to 20 percent higher. In this book, when variations of decimals and arabic numbers are of some consequence, they have been listed in the table for the model number or commented upon in the text that follows.

Model Sizes

The second column in the tables is headed "Size." Over the years changes occurred when models were restyled or because of instability in the master mold. The net result is that there may be innumerable sizes even though this book shows a single height for any one given model/indicator line. For example, Little Fiddler, Hum. 4, is now listed in only one standard size, currently $4\frac{3}{4}''$ high. However, this model has been reported as small as 4'' high and as large as 6'' high. In order to de-emphasize this variation, we have elected to show only the standard size that is listed in the current Hummelwerk catalog. Oversized and undersized pieces are worth more to selective collectors than the standard size, but there are too many of these variations and too many collectors with too many differences of opinion to try to establish any nice easy rule to remember. Occasionally the book mentions what some differences are known to have been worth to some collectors.

Status

In the third, "Status" column, a number of symbols appear. The following key defines these symbols:

A   *Assigned Number.* One that has not been announced or cataloged for

The M.I. Hummel Pedigree

Model # / Size #
Little Goat Herder

Copyright Notice

TMK-2
FULL BEE

Country of Origin

Artist Mark

Production Control Number

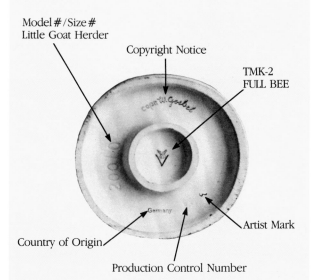

TMK-2B, Stamped Full Bee on base of Hear Ye, Hear Ye, Hum. 15/0. Has ® for registered mark, stamped black Germany, but no copyright year.

© Copyright Insignia

Model # / Size #
Just Resting

TMK-5C
Goebel Bee

Production Control Number

W. Germany Country of Origin

Copyright Year

Artist Mark

Year Decorated '79

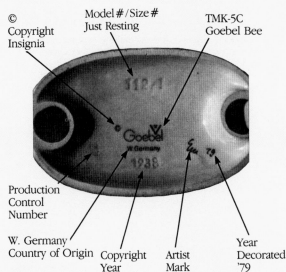

TMK-3A, Early Partial Stylized Bee stamped in incised circle with Western Germany stamped in black. Base of Volunteers, Hum. 50/0, with no copyright year or insignia.

TMK-3D, Small Stylized Transfer Bee in blue on base of Waiter, Hum. 154/1. With unusual artist initials, "O.S." and date, "11/62." Incised model number filled in with black.

TMK-4A, Small Stylized Bee Blue Transfer label on base of Umbrella Girl. Incised 152/II B with incised 1951 copyright year. W. Germany and company name in label.

TMK-5C, Blue Transfer Label overglaze, hand-dated, 79 on base of Just Resting, Hum. 112/I; incised 1938 copyright year.

TMK-6, Goebel (only) Blue Transfer Label overglaze; hand-dated, 79; on base of Spring Dance, Hum. 353/0 reissue.

sale but to which a design has already been allocated by Goebel as a possible future production item.

C   *Cancelled Number.* A number that the Goebel Company has used to identify a design but which they do not intend to use again.

D   *Discontinued Number.* This indicates a model that was once issued for sale but was later deleted from the catalog and is not currently available.

O   *Open Number.* A model number which at present is not allocated to any specific design; available for future use when the need arises.

P   *Produced Number.* P is a symbol used to indicate that at some time this model number was produced, cataloged, and offered for sale.

R   *Reissued Number.* This symbol describes a model that was once produced, then possibly discontinued, but (since 1978) is now being produced and cataloged for sale.

The Status columns sometime contain lowercase letters that follow the capital ones just described. The purpose of these is to refer the reader to important information at the bottom of the table. The notes are usually self-explanatory, so one example should suffice. Mother's Darling, Hum. 175, has been produced in two different colorings, and the scarcer of the two warrants a higher price. This bandanna'd little girl is carrying two large bags formed from kerchiefs. Initially her bandanna had no polka dots, and the large kerchief she was carrying in her right hand had a pink background decorated with blue polka dots, while the one in her left hand was a light blue green with red polka dots. After restyling in the 1960s, the model appeared with white polka dots in her bandanna and both the bags had a light blue background.   As shown on page 93 a small letter "a" follows the first two listings which are now discontinued (D-a). The letter "a" below the table explains that those higher prices are for the old style. The letters P-b indicate the prices for the restyled model with light blue bags.

Prices of M.I. Hummel Figurines

As previously mentioned there are over one-hundred and thirty pages in this book that contain 4,000 different prices divided among six trademark columns, TMK-1 through TMK-6. These prices are published to help you arrive at a decision when buying, selling, or judging what a specific combination may be worth to you. We have seen persons at auctions using these prices as though they were ones posted on a gasoline pump. In other words, they thought that was the price they had to pay. Nothing could be further from reality. The dollar figures in the tables are only guides.

A little background on how these prices got in the book might further convince you that they are not as exact as the time on your digital watch. Since June, 1981, over twenty-five thousand prices obtained from "for sale" advertisements, copies of sales slips sent by gift shop dealers, results from antique shows and over fifty auctions all over the country, and, not least of all, the valued opinion of several of the top collectors in this country have been recorded on 5″ x 8″ cards, one card for each line item. These prices have been color-coded and lettered to show the exact place the sale occurred. From this accumulation of data we selected one price that either statistically appeared to represent a concensus or was the estimate of the experts. The spread between high and low for one trademark might range from a low of fifty dollars to a high of perhaps one-hundred and fifty. In most cases the very low prices were accompanied by notes indicating they were imperfect or otherwise defective. A high figure often resulted when two collectors at an auction were battling to get the piece. In our research quite a few pieces clustered around ninety to one-hundred dollars. We chose the hundred-dollar figure because the data were obtained during the recession and the cards have already indicated an upward movement in prices. An exception are the prices in column TMK-6. Invariably we used the suggested retail price as published by a principal Goebel distributor.

Some price guides use a high and low range for each item. The tables that follow can be used in the same manner by deducting 30 to 40 percent from the price given to arrive at the lower figure. This is what a dealer might pay if you were liquidating your collection. To obtain a top figure add 25 to 40 percent which might be paid by someone who was loaded (with money) or had not bothered to read this book.

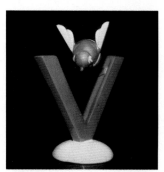

Insurance and Appraisals

Another reason for a single price is that the Internal Revenue Service and insurance companies require the use of a single dollar value for any one item. The I.R.S. says that a fair price is the figure agreed upon by an equally interested buyer and seller, and a fair value is what the prices are intended to represent. They have been used by appraisers for the I.R.S., F.B.I. (in one case), and have been accepted by most large insurance companies for the special policies that are ideal for protecting Hummel figurines and other collectibles. These policies are known as personal property floaters (attached to a homeowner's policy) or as separate fine arts policies. It is inadvisable to depend on a homeowner's policy. It does not cover breakage and will not pay a fair reimbursement unless the loss is substantiated by a recent sales slip.

These special types of policies require an attached, itemized appraisal list. Many insurance companies will accept the values from this book and agree to pay such if there is mysterious disappearance, robbery, fire, or breakage. If you are not conversant with how you can appraise your own collection and get this type of special policy you can do two things. One, read our standard reference book, *Hummel Art II* starting on page 229. Two, talk to your insurance agent or one that specializes in this type of policy. Insurance companies and their addresses are listed in the book.

M.I. Hummel Bust, HU-2. Large. Stamped with Three Line, TMK-4, and incised year "1967." Designed by "SKROBEK"; year discontinued unknown. Superseded by small 5¾" bust in 1977 with TMK-5.

The 𝓜.𝓙.𝓗𝓾𝓶𝓶𝓮𝓵® Collection by Goebel

The following pages contain, in numerical order, the complete collection of Sister Hummel's work that Goebel's master sculptors have adapted into figurines and other articles. If available, a picture of the model is shown together with the model number, name, and table showing essential specifications and prices that apply. This is followed by historical information. The table at the top needs some explanation to be of maximum value to the reader. Each table has six columns headed by TMK-1 through 6. The figures in these columns represent the present insurable value of that model and size. In some cases there is only a dash mark (—) rather than a value in dollars. This indicates that it is unlikely an example in that size and trademark will be found. It does not mean there are NONE. Since our first publication many readers and others have found examples that were previously unknown. Question marks may appear alone or sometimes after a dollar value. These indicate that there is reasonable doubt that a piece has been documented. The tables present the information so that the collector can get a mental picture of the production history of any model produced.

Three-dimensional prototype of TMK-2 derived from design by Sister Hummel. Photographed at the Hummel Home, Massing, West Germany.

1 Puppy Love

Indicator	Size	Status	TMK-1	TMK-2	TMK-3	TMK-4	TMK-5	TMK-6
1	5"	D,a	350	250	—	—	—	—
1	5"	P,b	—	150	96	92	80	74

(a – looking down violin, no bow tie. b – looking to the right, bow tie.)

This is one of the first ten models shown by Goebel at the Leipzig Fair in Germany in 1935. John Schmid bought a dozen at that time to be sold in the U.S. for approximately $1 each. To this day, these pieces are found without a copyright date. The early catalog listed this piece as "Little Fiddler with Dog" until about 1959. This corresponds to the German name *Geigerlein mit Hund*. It is the same figure as both models of Little Fiddler, Hum. 2 and Hum. 4. *Note from Bruce from Germany 92/82 $52*

1 **Puppy Love** *with bow tie, TMK-5, no copyright date.*

2 Little Fiddler

Indicator	Size	Status	TMK-1	TMK-2	TMK-3	TMK-4	TMK-5	TMK-6
2.	5¼"	D	400	—	270	—	—	—
2/0	6"	P	325	210	125	110	97	90
2./0	6"	D	360	—	—	—	—	—
2/I	7½"	P,a	500	400	250	220	200	185
2/II	10¾"	P	1,250	1,000	800	700	650	600
2/III	12¼"	R	1,800	1,500	1,200	—	720	650
2/3	12¼"	D	2,000	1,800	—	—	—	—

(a – also found as 2/1. Add 10 percent for arabic.)

While this figurine is almost identical to Puppy Love, Hum. 1, and to Little Fiddler, Hum. 4, this model has some distinguishing characteristics. Hum. 2 has a brown hat and no dog. It is the only figurine of the three that was made in a range of sizes. Until about 1960, this figurine was known as "Little Fiddler without Dog," which corresponds to the German name *Geigerlein ohne Hund*. Verlag Emil Fink's postcard 203 is a reproduction of the original drawing.

2 **Little Fiddler,** *restyled, brown hat, TMK-5.*

3 Book Worm

Indicator	Size	Status	TMK-1	TMK-2	TMK-3	TMK-4	TMK-5	TMK-6
3/1	5½"	P	500	350	220	180	150	140
3/II(2)	8"	P,a	1,200	1,000	750	700	650	600
3/III(3)	9"	R,b	2,200	1,500	1,000	—	750	650

(a – also found as 3/2. Add 10 percent for arabic. Also found as 3/3. Add 10 percent for arabic. Reissued in 1978 as 3/III with TMK-5.)

This piece was adapted by Arthur Möller in 1935 from Sister Hummel's drawing. The two larger sizes were added at a later date. The only other name recorded so far is "The Bookworm," a translation of the German *Der Bücherwurm*. Figure is also used as one of the bookends, Hum 14 A. Hum 14 A book is not colored. Bookend has a hole with stopper in the bottom for filling with sand.

3/I **Book Worm,** *with book pictures in color, TMK-5.*

4 Little Fiddler

Indicator	Size	Status	TMK-1	TMK-2	TMK-3	TMK-4	TMK-5	TMK-6
4	4¾"	P,a	275	150	100	80	70	65

(a – when found as 4. (decimal) with TMK-1, $300.)

This is the same figure as Hum. 2, except for the distinguishing black instead of brown hat. While issued in only one size, it has been reported as small as 4¼" and as large as 6" high. Thus it is possible to put together an ascending set of Little Fiddler figurines from about 4" to over 12" high. This has the same German name as Hum. 2. Verlag Emil Fink produces a large graphic and postcard as 101A from the original drawing.

4 **Little Fiddler**, *black hat, 4¾" high,* *TMK-5.*

5 Strolling Along

Indicator	Size	Status	TMK-1	TMK-2	TMK-3	TMK-4	TMK-5	TMK-6
5	4¾"	D,a	275	175	—	—	—	—
5	4¾"	P,b	—	—	100	85	72	65

(a – head turned to the left, eyes to the right. b – head to the left, eyes straight toward viewer.)

Here is another early adaptation done in 1935 by Arthur Möller, master sculptor. The footnotes above describe the position of the boy's head. There are minor color variations of the dog. This piece is similar to Hum. 7 and to Hum. 11, Merry Wanderer, as its German name implies, *Wanderbub mit Hund* (Wanderer with Dog). No original drawing with a boy and the dog has yet been located.

5 **Strolling Along**, *restyled version,* *TMK-5.*

6 Sensitive Hunter

Indicator	Size	Status	TMK-1	TMK-2	TMK-3	TMK-4	TMK-5	TMK-6
6/0	4¾"	P,b	—	—	100	75	70	65
6/0	4¾"	D,a	175	—	—	—	—	—
6.	5"	D,a	400	—	—	—	—	—
6/I	5½"	P,b	375	200	160	120	100	85
6/II	7½"	P,b	700	400	225	220?	200	175

(a – suspenders form "H" in back. b – suspenders form "X" in back.)

Originally introduced in 1935. In the 1950s it was listed as 6 (only). The older model commands a premium because of the "H" suspenders. The German name is *Jägerlein* or "Little Hunter." Another companion hunter is Good Hunting, Hum. 307. The color of the rabbit has been changed to natural brown in TMK-6.

6/1 **Sensitive Hunter**, *"X" straps,* *TMK-5.*

7 Merry Wanderer

Indicator	Size	Status	TMK-1	TMK-2	TMK-3	TMK-4	TMK-5	TMK-6
7/0	6¼"	P	300	225	130	120	100	90
7/I(1)	7"	P,a	600	500	275	225	200	185
7/II(2)	9½"	P	1,500	1,000	750	700	650	600
7/III(3)	11¼"	P	2,000	1,600	900	800	720	650
7/X	32"	P	—	—	—	—	12,400	12,400

(a – add 50 percent for 7/I found with double base. Add 10 percent for arabic 1 and 2.)

This must be the most widely publicized M.I. Hummel figurine. It appears in a ten-foot version to welcome visitors to the Goebel plant in Rödental. Another equally impressive replica is in front of the beautiful mansion in Tarrytown, New York, the headquarters of the Goebel Collectors' Club. The sizes and marks available are detailed above. Hum. 7/II, issued in the early 1970s, was restyled by Gerhard Skrobek. Hum. 7/III, also restyled, was reintroduced in the 1978 and 1979 catalogs. Hum. 7/X, modeled some years earlier, was first introduced in the U.S. about 1976.

7/0 Merry Wanderer, *6" high,* TMK-5.

8 Book Worm

Indicator	Size	Status	TMK-1	TMK-2	TMK-3	TMK-4	TMK-5	TMK-6
8	4"	P	350	200	120	110	95	84

Same as figurine Hum. 3. It is the smallest size produced and is listed in early catalogs before World War II. It is unknown at this time why this smaller size was given a completely different Hummel number rather than the more normal Hum. 3/0. This piece has colored book pages, while its counterpart, Hum. 14 A, one of the Book Worm Bookends, does not.

8 Book Worm, *book pictures in color,* TMK-5.

9 Begging His Share

Indicator	Size	Status	TMK-1	TMK-2	TMK-3	TMK-4	TMK-5	TMK-6
9(.)	5½"	D,a	500	400	300	—	—	—
9	5½"	P,b	—	—	160	110	95	84

(a – hole in cake for candle. b – no hole in cake. Add 10 percent for decimal.)

While this is found in all trademarks and probably was designed in 1935, this model was missing from the 1947 and 1950 catalogs. Until it was restyled in the mid-1960s, the large hole in the center of the cake served as a candleholder. After that time it was issued with only a very small indentation in the center. The German name is *Gratulant,* or "The Well-Wisher." This forms another one of the group of figures sought after by dog owners — especially those owning schnauzers.

9 Begging His Share, *no candle socket,* TMK-5.

10 Flower Madonna

Indicator	Size	Status	TMK-1	TMK-2	TMK-3	TMK-4	TMK-5	TMK-6
10/I	8″ - 9″	D,o,b	500	300	—	—	—	—
10/I	8″ - 9″	D,o,w	400	200	—	—	—	—
10/I	8″ - 9″	P,c,b	—	—	170	160	140	125
10/I	8″ - 9″	P,c,w	—	—	100	85	75	65
10/III	12″ +	D,o,b	850	750	—	—	—	—
10/III	12″ +	D,o,w	500	300	—	—	—	—
10/III	12″ +	D,o,v	3,000+	2,000+	—	—	—	—
10/III	12″ +	D,c,b,t	2,500	1,500+	400	350	325	300
10/III	12″ +	D,c,w,t	—	—	225	185	175	165

(b – blue color. c – closed halo. o – open halo. t – temporarily withdrawn, reinstated later. v – various colors — brown, ivory, dark blue, yellow. w – white glaze. + – prices and sizes vary widely. Add 10 percent for arabic.)

10/1 **Flower Madonna** *with flat halo, TMK-5.*

The earliest catalogs list the two sizes at approximately 8″ and 11″, although other size molds must have been used because of the wide range of sizes found. The other known colors are an antiqued caramel color, an aqua with a burnished gold leaf halo, a pastel blue, a reddish brown, and a creamy ivory. Until about 1955, the halo was open in the back and is referred to as the "doughnut halo." The redesigned piece was introduced with a solid halo.

11 Merry Wanderer

Indicator	Size	Status	TMK-1	TMK-2	TMK-3	TMK-4	TMK-5	TMK-6
11/2/0	4¼″	D,a	—	200	—	—	—	—
11/2/0	4¼″	P	200	125	80	65	58	53
11/0	4¾″	P	275	150	100	85	75	68
11	4¾″	D	300	—	—	—	—	—
11.	4¾″	D	325	275	—	—	—	—

(a – six-button vest in TMK-2.)

11/0 **Merry Wanderer,** *5″ high, TMK-5.*

Refer to Hum. 7, Merry Wanderer, for the complete story of this motif. Hum. 11 has been found with 11. (decimal) in TMK-1, and 11/2/0 is known with a six-button vest in TMK-2. The original drawings Sister Hummel did of this highly publicized motif are owned by Verlag Emil Fink, who has produced postcard 202 and print 101B from the original.

12 Chimney Sweep

Indicator	Size	Status	TMK-1	TMK-2	TMK-3	TMK-4	TMK-5	TMK-6
12/2/0	4″	P	120	75	50	45	41	37
12/I	5½″	P	300	140	95	85	75	69
12(.)	6¼″	D,a	375	250	—	—	—	—

(a – add 10 percent for decimal.)

12/I **Chimney Sweep,** *TMK-4.*

This figurine has been made since before World War II and is found in a wide variation of heights from the ones listed above. For example, in the 1950 catalog, "Smoky" and the German name *Schornsteinfeger* were listed as 14.5 cm or 6″ high for the 12/I size. The original drawing, owned by Ars Edition, has been published as graphic H 261. Goebel has also sold another Chimney Sweep figurine designed by a different artist, which has confused some collectors because of similar company trademarks. All genuine Hummels are incised with the M.I. Hummel facsimile signature.

13 Meditation

Indicator	Size	Status	TMK-1	TMK-2	TMK-3	TMK-4	TMK-5	TMK-6
13/2/0	4½″	P	—	95	72	67	59	53
13/0	5½″	P	300	150	95	85	77	70
13	7″	D,a	3,000	—	—	—	—	—
13/II	7″	R,b	—	—	—	—	220	200
13/II(2)	7″	D,a,c	2,000	1,800	—	—	—	—
13/V	13¾″	R	—	2,000	1,500	1,000	715	650

(a – flowers in basket. b – no flowers in basket. c – add 15 percent for arabic.)

13/0 Meditation, *no flowers in basket,*
TMK-5.

Hum. 13 is known with all trademarks and an uncertain variety of copyright dates in sizes from 4″ to 14″ high. According to factory records, the 7″ size Hum. 13/II was restyled about 1962, which eliminated the flowers from the rear of the basket. However, the largest size, 13¾″, unavailable for some time, was cataloged again in 1978 with a full basket of flowers. This larger size carries a 1957 copyright in some cases. It was once called "The Well Wisher," similar to the present German name *Die Gratulantin.* The original drawing owned by Fink is available in postcard 201.

14 A&B Book Worm, Bookends

Indicator	Size	Status	TMK-1	TMK-2	TMK-3	TMK-4	TMK-5	TMK-6
14 A&B	5½″	P	500	350	250	220	200	180

14 A&B Book Worm Bookends, *no color in pictures, TMK-5.*

The girl figure in this pair is similar to Hum. 3 and Hum. 8, with two visible exceptions. The picture in the book is monochrome. It is in full color in the figurine. The bottom of the bookend has a hole (closed by either an older cork or a modern plastic stopper) for filling with sand and lead shot for weight to support books. In January 1980, a motif similar to the bookend boy was introduced on the 1980 Annual Bell, Hum. 702. The bell is named "Thoughtful." See Hum. 415, figurine introduced in 1981.

15 Hear Ye, Hear Ye

Indicator	Size	Status	TMK-1	TMK-2	TMK-3	TMK-4	TMK-5	TMK-6
15/0	5″	P	300	200	125	110	95	84
15/I(1)	6″	P,b	300	200	140	115	105	95
15/II(2)	7″	P,b	600	400	275	230	205	185
15	7¼″	D,a	1,200	—	—	—	—	—

(a – with brown mittens. b – add 10 percent for arabic.)

This colorful and popular figurine designed in the 1930s was introduced in the smaller 5″ size before World War II as "Nightwatchman." It is listed in the 1947 catalog under that name at 5½″ high. Sometime before the 1959 catalog it was produced in two larger sizes. Early trademarks have a baby blue metal blade versus gray. The figurine matches the bas-relief design on the 1972 Annual Plate, Hum. 265. The original drawing is owned by Ars Edition and is cataloged as H 597.

15/I Hear Ye, Hear Ye, *TMK-5.*

16 Little Hiker

Indicator	Size	Status	TMK-1	TMK-2	TMK-3	TMK-4	TMK-5	TMK-6
16/3/0	4″	D	—	2,500	—	—	—	—
16/2/0	4½″	P	160	90	65	55	47	42
16.	5½″	D,a	350	250	—	—	—	—
16	6″	D	325	—	—	—	—	—
16/I(1)	6″	P	280	150	95	85	77	70

(a – add 10 percent for decimal.)

16/I Little Hiker, *TMK-3.*

The Little Hiker is also called "Happy Go Lucky," *Hans im Glück,* or "Hans in Fortune." First issued around the time of World War II, it was listed as being available in 16/2/0 and 16/I sizes as early as 1950. An Illinois collector has the figurine with a rare "roof" over the dot in the Crown mark, TMK-1. No major variations or redesigning have been reported to date. The original drawing by Sister Hummel is owned by Ars Edition and issued as graphic H 309.

17 Congratulations

Indicator	Size	Status	TMK-1	TMK-2	TMK-3	TMK-4	TMK-5	TMK-6
17/0	6″	D,a	—	—	100	85	75	—
17/0	6″	D,b	300	225	175	—	—	—
17	6″	P,a	—	—	—	—	—	63
17/I	?	U	—	—	—	—	—	—
17/II(2)	8″	D,b	5,000	4,000	3,000	—	—	—

(a – with socks. b – without socks.)

17/0 **Congratulations,** *no socks, TMK-3.*

Currently produced only in the 6″ size and incised 17 only, this model was originally found in this size marked 17/0. At one time, it was produced in the 8″ size and marked either 17/II or 17/2 (arabic). The 8″ size and the older marks of the 6″ size are found without socks. Socks were added sometime in the early 1970s. Some Crown pieces have a handle of horn pointed toward the back of the figurine. The original drawing is owned by Ars Edition, who produces graphic H 454 from it. The German name is *Ich Gratulier* or "I Congratulate."

18 Christ Child

Indicator	Size	Status	TMK-1	TMK-2	TMK-3	TMK-4	TMK-5	TMK-6
18	2″ × 6″	P	175	120	75	60	55	50
18	2″ × 6″	D,a	350	—	—	—	—	—

(a – in white overglaze.)

18 **Christ Child,** *TMK-3.*

The figurine on a pallet without a halo can be distinguished from Infant Jesus, Hum. 214/A/K, which has a halo, and from Infant of Krumbad, Hum. 78, which is not lying on a pad or pallet and also has no halo. Hum. 18 has been made in only the one size but the early catalogs show the size about ½″ larger in both dimensions. An uncataloged rarity is the same figure in white overglaze. The 1950 catalog not only lists this model as larger but refers to it as "Christmas Night," apparently from the assigned German name of *Still Nacht, Jesuskind,* or "Silent Night, Baby Jesus."

19   Cancelled

Indicator	Size	Status	TMK-1	TMK-2	TMK-3	TMK-4	TMK-5	TMK-6
19	?		—	—	—	—	—	—

A factory record suggests that this was similar to Prayer Before Battle, Hum. 20, done by master modeler Arthur Möller in 1935, but it was not approved by the convent and therefore never issued. No record of a prototype was found in the factory, nor have any been reported from other sources. If ever discovered, the value would be in the mid five-digit range.

20 Prayer Before Battle, *TMK-5.*

20   Prayer Before Battle

Indicator	Size	Status	TMK-1	TMK-2	TMK-3	TMK-4	TMK-5	TMK-6
20	4½″	P,a	275	150	99	85	75	69
20.	4½″	D,b	300	—	—	—	—	—

(a – open horn. b – closed horn.)

This model was adapted by Arthur Möller in 1935 from Sister Hummel's original drawing. A 1950 catalog lists the size as 4″ high, while the current catalogs list it as 4½″. It is found in all trademarks and there seem to have been only minor variations over the course of the years. The demand for this piece usually appears to be in excess of the supply. The German name of *Der fromme Reitersmann* translates as "The Pious Horseman." The original drawing has been lithographed by Ars Edition as graphic H 165. Prayer Before Battle is also one-half of the pair of bookends, Hum. 76 A&B, with 76 A being Doll Mother.

21/I Heavenly Angel, *TMK-5.*

21   Heavenly Angel

Indicator	Size	Status	TMK-1	TMK-2	TMK-3	TMK-4	TMK-5	TMK-6
21/0	4¾″	P	170	130	60	50	45	40
21/0/½	6″	P	275	175	110	90	80	70
21	?	U	—	—	—	—	—	—
21/I	6¾″	P	300	200	125	100?	90	84
21/II(2)	8¾″	P	750	400	240	200	185	175

This design is recognized by hundreds of thousands of collectors and dealers because it was used as the bas-relief design on the first M.I. Hummel Annual Plate, Hum. 264, in 1971. This figurine is now in great demand for its own merit and also as a companion piece to display in a shadow box along with the 1971 plate. The name in the 1950s catalog was "Little Guardian" or *Christkindlein kommt* in German. While the two larger sizes seem to have been introduced later, they have been reported with all trademarks. This figurine, in white overglaze, is valued at two to three times the standard colored model. An original drawing of this motif is now owned by Ars Edition and reproduced by them as graphic H 444. Emil Fink produces postcard 842.

22 Sitting Angel with Birds, Holy Water Font

Indicator	Size	Status	TMK-1	TMK-2	TMK-3	TMK-4	TMK-5	TMK-6
22/0	3½″	P	100	75	35	25	21	17
22.	4″	D	150	—	—	—	—	—
22/I	5″	D	300	250	200	—	—	—

The title of this font has been expanded to accommodate both the original German name, *Weihkessel, sitzender Engel*, and the name in the U.S. catalogs, "Angel with Birds," because many fonts appear with only minor design modifications of small children or angels, some with wings and some without. Over the years, slight but not necessarily important changes have been made in color, design, and shape of the bowl.

22 Sitting Angel with Birds, *Holy Water Font, TMK-3; alternate name, Sitting Angel.*

23 Adoration

Indicator	Size	Status	TMK-1	TMK-2	TMK-3	TMK-4	TMK-5	TMK-6
23.	6″	D	700	400	—	—	—	—
23/I	6¼″	P,a	425	350	275	—	—	—
23/I	6¼″	P,b	—	—	—	185	160	147
23/(2)	7½″	D,a	—	1,200	—	—	—	—
23/III(3)	9″	P,c	700	450	280	250	230	210

(a – flowers on side of table. b – no flowers on side of table. c – add 20 percent for arabic.)

The smaller size 23/I was listed as early as 1950 and at that time was only 6¼″ high. Only one report is known of this motif in the 23/II size, which was marked 23/2 (arabic) and was 7½″ high. Both 23/I and 23/III were made in rare, white overglaze and valued in the low four-digit range. In 1978, the large size was restyled in the modern textured finish, probably by Gerhard Skrobek. Hum. 23 has also been cataloged as "At the Shrine," "Ave Maria," and the German name of *Bei Mutter Maria, Marterl,* which translates as "At Mother Maria's." The original drawing is owned by Verlag Emil Fink. Postcard 839 is published by them, as are prints 100A and 100G.

23/I Adoration, *TMK-5.*

24 Lullaby, Candleholder

Indicator	Size	Status	TMK-1	TMK-2	TMK-3	TMK-4	TMK-5	TMK-6
24	5″	D	400	—	—	—	—	—
24/I	5″	D,a	—	600	—	—	—	—
24/I(1)	5″	P	400	200	120	100	85	74
24/III(3)	8″	D,b	1,200	800	400	350	310	270

(a – unusual all-white overglaze. b – temporarily withdrawn, but to be reinstated.)

This piece has been produced with two different diameter candles in the small and large sizes. Hum. 24 was found marked 24 (only). This same design was issued later as Heavenly Lullaby figurine, Hum. 262, without the candle socket. The rare 24/III was reinstated in 1978 in Germany and Canada. It immediately sold at premium prices. This is an adaptation of Ars Edition graphic, H 625.

24/III Lullaby, *Candleholder, TMK-3 (see 262).*

25 Angelic Sleep, Candleholder

Indicator	Size	Status	TMK-1	TMK-2	TMK-3	TMK-4	TMK-5	TMK-6
25	5"	P	300	200	150	98	88	80

Apparently this similar piece is only found incised 25, even though some catalogs as recently as 1979 and 1980 list it as 25/I, with the same dimensions. This piece was believed to have been issued sometime in the 1940s. According to the German name of *Stille Nacht mit Kerzentülle*, this would have been still another group called "Silent Night," now used in connection with Hum. 31 and Hum. 54 candleholders. The original drawing is owned by Ars Edition, who has published graphic H 487.

25 Angelic Sleep, *Candleholder, no trademark.*

26 Child Jesus, Holy Water Font

Indicator	Size	Status	TMK-1	TMK-2	TMK-3	TMK-4	TMK-5	TMK-6
26/0	5"	P,a	80	50	35	25	20	17
26/0	5"	D,b	800	—	—	—	—	—
26/I	6"	P,a	350	250	200	—	—	—
26/I	6"	D,b	1,000	—	—	—	—	—
26/I	6"	D,c	1,200	—	—	—	—	—

(*a – red dress, no scalloped edge. b – red dress, scalloped edge. c – blue dress, scalloped edge.*)

When first issued this figure had a light blue gown (as shown in the photograph on this page). Later, the color was changed to the present dark red color. The two sizes, about 5" and 6" high, were listed as early as the 1950 catalog. This larger size 26/I is scarce and difficult to find. This design has also been called "Christ Child." The German name is *Weihkessel, Christkindlein,* or "Child Jesus, Holy Water Font." Prints have been published from the original drawing owned by Ars Edition as H 498.

26/0 Child Jesus, *Holy Water Font, rare blue gown.*

27 Joyous News, Candleholder

Indicator	Size	Status	TMK-1	TMK-2	TMK-3	TMK-4	TMK-5	TMK-6
27/I	2¾"	D	350	—	—	—	—	—
27/3	4½"	D	1,500	1,200	1,000?	—	—	—
27/III	4½"	R	—	—	—	—	100	90

Similar designs are: Angel, Joyous News with Trumpet, III/40; Little Gabriel, a standing figurine, Hum. 32; and Angel with Trumpet, 238 C, which is part of Angel Trio B. Hum. 27 was only available at high prices in the secondary market until 1978 when it was reinstated in the 27/III size as a figurine. It is still considered rare with TMK-1 or 2. Beginning collectors should use caution in paying high prices in the secondary market because of the "lookalikes" and the larger reinstated size. The German name of *O, du fröhliche* translates as "O, You Joyful One."

27/I Joyous News, *Candleholder, rare, TMK-1, Miller Collection.*

28 Wayside Devotion

Indicator	Size	Status	TMK-1	TMK-2	TMK-3	TMK-4	TMK-5	TMK-6
28/II(2)	7½″	P	700	500	275	200	175	157
28	8″	D	1,000	—	—	—	—	—
28/III(3)	8¾″	P	900	550	350	300	250	220

Size 28/II was listed as only 7″ high in the 1950 catalog. This model has been reported in the arabic 2, as has the larger size in the arabic 3, each of which would be valued at 15 percent more than the price list shows for the Roman numbers. This design without the shrine is called Eventide, Hum. 99. It has also been referred to as "The Little Shepherd," and "Evening Song," which is the translation for the German name, *Abendlied, Marterl.* The original drawing is owned by Ars Edition, who has published graphic H 383.

28/II Wayside Devotion, *TMK-3.*

29 Guardian Angel, Holy Water Font

Indicator	Size	Status	TMK-1	TMK-2	TMK-3	TMK-4	TMK-5	TMK-6
29/0	6″	D	1,400	1,200	1,000	—	—	—
29.	6″	D	1,500	—	—	—	—	—
29/I	6½″	D	1,800	1,500	—	—	—	—

This design was discontinued, probably in the late 1950s, and replaced by Kneeling Angel, Hum. 248. The unsupported wings of Hum. 29 were too easily damaged, so they were backed up and closed, as Hum. 248. It was still being listed in original form in a 1959 U.S. catalog and, therefore, should be found with the first three trademarks. The factory records show this as having been produced in the three sizes, although examples are very scarce. The older catalogs refer to all of the fonts as merely "Holy Water Fonts" with no further descriptive name.

29 Guardian Angel, *Holy Water Font (see 248), TMK-1, courtesy W. Goebel Co.*

30 A&B Ba-Bee Rings

Indicator	Size	Status	TMK-1	TMK-2	TMK-3	TMK-4	TMK-5	TMK-6
30 A&B	4¾″	P	—	—	—	—	90	84
30/0/A&B	5″	P	300	250	150	125?	—	—
30/1/A&B	6″	D,a	2,000	—	—	—	—	—
30/1/A&B	6″	D,b	5,000+	—	—	—	—	—

(a – cream color. b – bright red.)

These were originally issued in the late 1930s and called "Hummel Rings" until the 1950s. They are currently incised only 30 A and 30 B. The other sizes listed above are earlier marks. This change is believed to have been made sometime in the 1950s when the name was changed. The boy, 30 A, and the girl, 30 B, rings are distinguished by the direction they face and the blue ribbon on the girl model. What is believed to be the only known 30/I B in bisque color was reported by Arbenz in the *Plate Collector* in October, 1980. Their German name, *Hui, die Hummel, Junge und Madchen, Wandringe* means "Oh, the Hummel boy and girl wall rings." The original drawing is owned by Ars Edition, who has produced graphic H 101 from it.

30/A Ba-Bee Ring, *TMK-5.*

31 Advent Group with Black Child (Silent Night), *Candleholder, rare, TMK-1, incised and stamped.*

31 Advent Group with Black Child (Silent Night), Candleholder

Indicator	Size	Status	TMK-1	TMK-2	TMK-3	TMK-4	TMK-5	TMK-6
31	3½″	D	9,000	—	—	—	—	—

At present, an estimated four or five pieces have been found which show a black child at the left without shoes or stockings. The child also wears a gold earring in his left ear. Sister Hummel's original drawing shows two black children to the left, a white angle, and a white holy child. This model is easily confused with Hum. 54 which is another candelholder that has recently been found with a black child in the same position but with shoes. Another similar group is Heavenly Song, Hum. 113, discontinued in 1981. At this time, it is assumed that they all originated with modifications from the drawings done by Sister Hummel that are owned by Ars Edition, graphics H 624, H 625, and H 626.

32/0 Little Gabriel, *TMK-3.*

32 Little Gabriel

Indicator	Size	Status	TMK-1	TMK-2	TMK-3	TMK-4	TMK-5	TMK-6
32/0	5″	D	250	150	100	75?	70	—
32	5″	P	375	300	?	?	60	53
32/I	6″	D	1,200	1,000	800	?	—	—

While current catalogs list this model as Hum. 32, factory records show that older models were originally produced as Hum. 32/0 about 5″ high, and also as 32/I about 6″ high. The dates these were discontinued have not been established. Recently, 32/0 has been reported in TMK-5. Sister Hummel's original drawing was made of a similar standing figure and is owned by Ars Edition, H 431. The German name is *0, du fröhliche, Engle* or "Oh, You Joyful Angel."

33 Joyful, *Ashtray, TMK-3.*

33 Joyful, Ashtray

Indicator	Size	Status	TMK-1	TMK-2	TMK-3	TMK-4	TMK-5	TMK-6
33	3½″	P	250	120	95	80	70	63

This figure was apparently used on the ashtray before it became the separate figurine, Joyful, Hum. 53, or the Candy Box, Hum. III/53. Designed and issued before 1950, it is found in all trademarks with minor variations. The German name is *Ascher, Gesangsprobe,* or "Ashtray, Singing Rehearsal." Another reported name is "Boy with Mandolin and Bird." The original drawing for all of these related issues is owned by Ars Edition. It is available as graphic H 385.

Key to Symbols: A — Assigned; C — Cancelled; D — Discontinued; O — Open; P — Produced; R — Reissued; (?) Examples Doubtful; (—) Examples Unlikely.

34 Singing Lesson, Ashtray

Indicator	Size	Status	TMK-1	TMK-2	TMK-3	TMK-4	TMK-5	TMK-6
34	3½"	P	300	130	110	90	85	75

Hum. 34 is found in all trademarks with little variation in size, design, and coloring. A 1950 U.S. catalog refers to this piece as "Ashtray, Boy with Raven," which highlights the difference between the ashtray and the figurine, Hum. 63. The ashtray is the only adaptation of this motif that shows a raven. All the others use a differently shaped yellow bird. When Sister Hummel made her original drawing, which is now owned by Ars Edition, it was done with a yellow bird up in a tree as depicted on the 1979 Plate. The German name is *Ash, 's stimmt net,* or "It's Not Right." The original drawing is reproduced by Ars Edition as H 146.

34 Singing Lesson, *Ashtray, TMK-5.*

35 The Good Shepherd, Holy Water Font

Indicator	Size	Status	TMK-1	TMK-2	TMK-3	TMK-4	TMK-5	TMK-6
35/0	4¾"	P	90	60	35	25	20	17
35	5"	D	400	—	—	—	—	—
35/I	5½"	D	300	200	100?	—	—	—

Apparently, the first version of this font issued before World War II was incised with only the whole number, 35. This size was later cataloged as 35/I, also 5½" high. By 1950, a smaller size, 35/0, 4¾" high, was for sale at the time. For information on the original drawing and graphics available, see Hum. 42. Its German name, *Der gute Hirte,* translates the same as the English name. The original drawing is owned by Ars Edition. Graphics were produced as H 499.

35/0 The Good Shepherd, *Holy Water Font, TMK-5.*

36 Angel (Child) with Flowers, Holy Water Font

Indicator	Size	Status	TMK-1	TMK-2	TMK-3	TMK-4	TMK-5	TMK-6
36/0	4"	P	90	60	35	25	20	17
36	4¼"	D	150	—	—	—	—	—
36.	4¼"	D	200	—	—	—	—	—
36/I	4½"	D	200	150	100?	—	—	—

This font is usually cataloged and referred to as "Angel with Flowers," although it has also been recorded in German as *Kind mit Blumen,* or "Child with Flowers," which is a more accurate name. Since the halo indicates spirituality, it has been listed as Angel and Child in this book, to minimize confusion. Some modifications in design, color, and size have occurred over the years. In some cases, the rim of the halo is plain, in others ribbed. The shoes are either black or brown. These changes have not been associated with any trademarks.

36 Angel (Child) with Flowers, *Holy Water Font, TMK-1, incised and stamped.*

37 Herald Angels, Candleholder

37 Herald Angels, *Candleholder,*
TMK-5.

Indicator	Size	Status	TMK-1	TMK-2	TMK-3	TMK-4	TMK-5	TMK-6
37	3″	P,a	275	175	125	100	90	80
37	3″	D,b	350	250	175?	—	—	—

(a – candleholder socket is ½″ high. b – candleholder socket is 1″ high.)

When first issued, the candle socket in the center was over 1″ high. At some indefinite date, the height of the candle socket was reduced to about ½″ high. The similarity between the horn player and Joyous News, Hum. 27, is obvious. The German name for this Herald Angel group on a common base is *Adventsleuchter mid drei Engeln,* or "Advent Candleholder with Three Angles." There are no other forms of Hummel Art of this composite group known to date.

38 Angel, Joyous News with Lute

**III/38/0 Angel, Joyous News with
Lute,** *Candleholder, TMK-5, Trio (A).*

Indicator	Size	Status	TMK-1	TMK-2	TMK-3	TMK-4	TMK-5	TMK-6
I/38/0	2″	D	100	75	50	—	—	—
III/38/0	2″	P	75	50	35	30	25	22
III/38/I	2¾″	D	150?	100	75?	—	—	—

Since the late 1930s, this has been issued in the two sizes shown, but not always concurrently. The smaller size 38/0 was produced with two different sized candle sockets. The small size candle socket is 6mm in diameter; the larger socket is 1 cm in diameter. This socket size difference is sometimes designated in catalogs with a prefix. The candle sizes I and III are not incised on the figurines. This has also been known as "The Little Advent Angel with Lute" with the German name merely "Advent Angel with Lute" or *Adventsengelchen mit Laute.*

39 Angel, Joyous News with Accordion

Indicator	Size	Status	TMK-1	TMK-2	TMK-3	TMK-4	TMK-5	TMK-6
I/39/0	2″	D	100	75	50	—	—	—
III/39/0	2″	P	75	50	35	30	25	22
III/39/I	2¾″	D	150?	100	75?	—	—	—

The remarks about Hum. 38 pertain to Hum. 39, also, except for the name and design. There are no other "lookalikes" for this one of the group called Angel Trio A, Candleholders. These three, Hum. 38, 39, and 40, are usually priced as a group, but sold separately at one-third of the total price.

**III/39/0 Angel, Joyous News with
Accordion,** *Candleholder, TMK-5,*
Trio (A).

40 Angel, Joyous News with Trumpet

Indicator	Size	Status	TMK-1	TMK-2	TMK-3	TMK-4	TMK-5	TMK-6
I/40/0	2"	D	100	75	50	—	—	—
III/40/0	2"	P	75	50	35	30	25	22
III/40/I	2¾"	D	150	100	—	—	—	—

See Hum. 38 and 39 for common remarks. It is important to note the difference between Hum. 40 and the vary rare, discontinued Joyous News, Hum. 27/1. Besides the several thousand dollars difference in price, the candle socket in Hum. 40 is attached to the right hip, whereas in Hum. 27/1 it is attached at the right or left knee. Hum. 40 is also sold as part of a set and cataloged that way. The original drawing is owned by Ars Edition. Graphics of the original are produced as H 435 by them.

III/40/0 Angel with Trumpet, *Candleholder, TMK-5, Trio (A).*

41 Cancelled Number

Indicator	Size	Status	TMK-1	TMK-2	TMK-3	TMK-4	TMK-5	TMK-6
41	?		—	—	—	—	—	—

Recent research of the factory records by collector Robert Miller indicates that this number was provisionally assigned to a design similar to the ashtray Singing Lesson, Hum. 34, but, after further consideration, it was cancelled in October of 1935. No prototypes or examples have yet to be found. If the improbable discovery should happen, the value would probably be somewhere in the low four-digit range. Since prototypes of other cancelled numbers (Hum. 77) have been found in private hands, someday an example of Hum. 41 may be available for illustrating.

42 Good Shepherd

Indicator	Size	Status	TMK-1	TMK-2	TMK-3	TMK-4	TMK-5	TMK-6
42/0	6¼"	D,a	3,500	3,000	2,000?	—	—	—
42/0	6¼"	D,b	5,000	4,000.	3,000	—	—	—
42	6¼"	P,a	350	—	—	—	70	63
42.	6¼"	D,a	375	—	—	—	—	—
42/I	7½"	D,a	3,000	2,000	—	—	—	—

(a – Rust-colored gown. b – rare, light blue gown.)

The German name *Der gute Hirte* translates essentially as "The Good Shepherd." This piece was designed in the mid-1930s and issued before World War II. Prints, catalog number H 499, of Sister Hummel's original drawing are now published and sold by Ars Edition.

42 Good Shepherd, *TMK-5.*

43 March Winds, *TMK-5*.

43　March Winds

Indicator	Size	Status	TMK-1	TMK-2	TMK-3	TMK-4	TMK-5	TMK-6
43	5″	P	220	140	80	70	60	53
43.	5″	D	250	—	—	—	—	—

While this has been made in only one size, incised 43, since being designed in the mid-1930s, numerous size variations are found. When issued, it carried the German name of *Lausbub* for "Rascal," the name given to it by Sister Hummel. This piece is being produced in graphics as H 317 from the original drawing which is owned by Ars Edition. A Dubler figurine made in the U.S. during World War II is similar to this motif, as is one of the "Our Children" series imported by Napco from Japan.

44 A Culprits, *Table Lamp, TMK-2*.

44 A　Culprits, Table Lamp

Indicator	Size	Status	TMK-1	TMK-2	TMK-3	TMK-4	TMK-5	TMK-6
M44	9½″	D	1,000	—	—	—	—	—
M44/A	9½″	P	450	350	300	250	225	195

"Out on a Limb" was used in U.S. Copyrights GP1820 and GP1821 on October 6, 1950. Speculation indicates that this lamp/figurine was issued prior to 44 B, Out of Danger. This is further supported by the 1935 copyright on 44 A and the 1936 date on 44 B. The original drawings have been reproduced in lithographs by Verlag Emil Fink in Stuttgart as postcard 223. Both the height and design of the lamps changed over the years.

44 B　Out of Danger, Table Lamp

Indicator	Size	Status	TMK-1	TMK-2	TMK-3	TMK-4	TMK-5	TMK-6
M44/B	9½″	P	450	350	300	250	225	195

The remarks about the other half of this pair apply except for the names which, in addition to "Out of Danger," were "Out on a Limb," "Girl in a Tree," and the German *In Sicherheit, Mädchen* for "Girl in Safety." This design carries an incised 1936 copyright date, a year later than 44 A. Research for this book has failed to locate any drawing that resembles these two motifs.

44 B Out of Danger, *Table Lamp, TMK-4*.

45   Madonna with Halo

Indicator	Size	Status	TMK-1	TMK-2	TMK-3	TMK-4	TMK-5	TMK-6
45.	10½"	D,a	175	—	—	—	—	—
45	10½"	D,a	150	100	—	—	—	—
45/0	10½"	P,a	80	60	40	35	30	25
45.	10½"	D,b	200	—	—	—	—	—
45	10½"	D,b	180	120	—	—	—	—
45/0	10½"	P,b	160	120	75	60	45	40
45/I	11¾"	P,b	200	150	100	80	60	50
45/I	11¾"	P,a	100	80	50	40	35	30
45/III	16¾"	P,a,t	200	150	90	80	75	70
45/III	16¾"	D,b,t	300	250	200	125	110	100

(a – in white overglaze. b – in pastel color. t – temporarily withdrawn, reinstated later.)

This piece has also been referred to in German as *Madonna mit Heiligenschein,* equivalent to its present name. Hum. 45 has been issued in an array of sizes since its introduction in the late 1930s. In catalogs, "13" indicates one decorated with a colored robe; "/W" indicates pieces finished in a white glaze; and "/6" indicates current pastel color. It has also been reported in pastel pink, ivory, and dark blue. Any madonna that is incised HM before the model/size designators is not a genuine M.I. Hummel but rather a madonna made by Goebel and created by one of their sculptors. Refer to "Goebel — Not Hummel Figurines," in *Hummel Art II.*

45/0 Madonna with Halo, *TMK-2.*

46   Madonna without Halo

Indicator	Size	Status	TMK-1	TMK-2	TMK-3	TMK-4	TMK-5	TMK-6
46.	10½"	D,a	175	—	—	—	—	—
46	10½"	D,a	150	100	—	—	—	—
46/0	10½"	P,a	80	60	40	35	30	25
46.	10½"	D,b	200	—	—	—	—	—
46	10½"	D,b	180	120	—	—	—	—
46/0	10½"	P,b	160	120	75	60	45	40
46/I	11¾"	P,b	200	150	100	80	60	50
46/I	11¾"	P,a	100	80	50	40	35	30
46/III	16¾"	P,a,t	200	150	90	80	75	70
46/III	16¾"	D,b,t	300	250	200	125	110	100

(a – in white overglaze. b – in pastel color. t – temporarily withdrawn, reinstated later.)

This version of the madonna created by Sister Hummel is available in a similar range of sizes and color finishes as is its counterpart, Hum. 45. In 1978 a very rare and unusual madonna in this design, made of terra-cotta or brick red material, was discovered by a very alert Hummel collector. For some unknown reason, it was incised "18" on the bottom and inscribed M.J.Hummel . It is pictured on this page along with a very similar piece, except for the added child. The right-hand piece was marked "Erphila" a contraction of Ebling & Reuss, Philadelphia, one of Goebel's distributors.

46/0 Madonna without Halo, *TMK-5.*

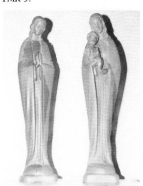
46 (L) Madonna without Halo, *incised M.I. Hummel, 18, stamped black "Made in Germany," rare terra-cotta. (R) Terra-cotta madonna and child, "HUMMEL" on bottom. Miller Collection.*

47/0 Goose Girl, *TMK-5.*

47 Goose Girl

Indicator	Size	Status	TMK-1	TMK-2	TMK-3	TMK-4	TMK-5	TMK-6
47/3/0	4″	P,a	—	125	90	80	70	63
47/0	4¾″	P,a	—	—	—	105	95	85
47./0	5″	D,b	350	300	—	—	—	—
47./0.	5″	D,b	425	—	—	—	—	—
47/0	5″	D,b	225	150	125	—	—	—
47/II	7″	P,a	450	350	300	250	210	190
47/2	7″	D,b	750	650	575	—	—	—
47./2	7″	D,b	850	750	—	—	—	—
47./2.	7″	D,b	950	—	—	—	—	—

(a – current design without "blade of grass" between geese. b – old design with "blade of grass" between geese.)

This model has been widely reproduced in porcelain and glass by various makers in the U.S., but WITHOUT the M.I. Hummel facsimile signature. Some of the earlier issues were made with a projection between the two geese painted green and referred to by collectors as a "blade of grass." Versions of Goose Girl in Serbian costume with 947/0 incised on the bottom are known. Sister Hummel's original drawing was produced as postcard 220 by Verlag Emil Fink.

48/0 Madonna, *Plaque (see 222), TMK-3.*

48 Madonna, Plaque

Indicator	Size	Status	TMK-1	TMK-2	TMK-3	TMK-4	TMK-5	TMK-6
48/0	4″	P	200	120	80	65	55	50
48/II(2)	6″	R	400	200	150	125	100	90
48/V(5)	10″	D	1,500	1,000	800	—	—	—

This bas-relief plaque is an adaptation of Sister Hummel's well-known drawing called the "Madonna in Red" which has received a wide distribution by Ars Edition. The intermediate size, 48/II, was reintroduced in 1978 in Germany, Canada, and the U.S. with TMK-5. The older marks are still scarce. See Hum. 222 for a similar plaque with wire frame. These plaques have also been called *Madonnenbild* in German, or "Madonna Picture."

49/0 To Market, *TMK-3.*

49 To Market

Indicator	Size	Status	TMK-1	TMK-2	TMK-3	TMK-4	TMK-5	TMK-6
49.3/0	4″	D	225	—	—	—	—	—
49/3/0	4″	P	—	130	110	95	82	74
49/0	5½″	P	300	200	160	135	125	110
49./0	5½″	D	400	300	—	—	—	—
49.	6¼″	R	1,000	—	—	—	400	—
49/I	6¼″	R	800	475	350	300	250	230

Old mark examples are very scarce, and reinstated figures with TMK-5 are incised 49 instead of the old marking, 49/I. Hum. 49/3/0, the smallest size, is produced without a bottle in the basket. No original drawing or graphic in this exact design has been located.

50 Volunteers

Indicator	Size	Status	TMK-1	TMK-2	TMK-3	TMK-4	TMK-5	TMK-6
50/2/0	5″	P	—	200	145	125	110	100
50/0	5½″	R	450	230	190	165?	145	130
50.	6½″	D	800	?	—	—	—	—
50/I	6½″	R	600	375	300	275?	250	230

The two larger sizes, 50/0 and 50/I, were not available in the U.S. for some years. These two pieces were reintroduced in 1979 with the TMK-5, some of which were dated "79" by the artist. The German name for this motif is *Soldatenspiel* or "Playing Soldiers." The original drawing is unlocated at present.

50/2/0 Volunteers, *TMK-5.*

51 Village Boy

Indicator	Size	Status	TMK-1	TMK-2	TMK-3	TMK-4	TMK-5	TMK-6
51/3/0	4″	P	—	85	50	45?	40	37
51/2/0	5¼″	P	150	100	90	70?	55	50
51.	5½″	D	325	—	—	—	—	—
51/0	6″	P	225	170	125	105?	93	84
51	?	D	300	220	—	—	—	—
51/I	7¼″	R	350	250	155	130?	115	105

Village Boy, 51/I, was reintroduced in 1978 in Germany and Canada in a limited quantity after being unavailable for some years. It was listed in the 1947 catalog. This piece was restyled with more sculptured hair and brighter colors, U.S. Copyright GF56, dated December 20, 1961, and incised with the 1961 date. The German name for Village Boy is *Dorfbub.* This appears to be the boy on the right in graphic F 665 published by Verlag Emil Fink.

51/2/0 Village Boy, *TMK-5.*

52 Going to Grandma's

Indicator	Size	Status	TMK-1	TMK-2	TMK-3	TMK-4	TMK-5	TMK-6
52/0	4¾″	P,a	300	275	225	—	—	—
52/0	4¾″	P,b	—	—	150	130	105	95
52./0	5″	D,a	300	275	—	—	—	—
52.	6¼″	D,a	1,000	—	—	—	—	—
52/I	6¼″	D,a	800	600	500	—	500	—
52/I	6¼″	R,b	—	—	—	—	255	230

(a – two figures on rectangular base. b – two figures on round base.)

It seems likely that the 52. (decimal) was replaced at some point by the 52/I as both are about 6¼″ high. In 1979, 52/I was reintroduced. Some examples may have the new artist's date, "79," and some may not. It still has the square base that was common to both old sizes. The small size, Hum. 52/0, was restyled and put on an oval base sometime in the 1960s. The smaller size has always contained cookies or candy in a cone. The larger sizes have an empty cone. The German name for this model is *Hausmütterchen,* or "Housemother." The original drawing has not been found.

52/0 Going to Grandma's, *TMK-5.*

53 Joyful, *TMK-5.*

53 Joyful

Indicator	Size	Status	TMK-1	TMK-2	TMK-3	TMK-4	TMK-5	TMK-6
53.	4"	D,a	750	—	—	—	—	—
53.	4"	D,b	250	200	—	—	—	—
53	4"	P,b	180	125	71	53	47	42

(a – with orange dress. b – with blue dress.)

Known earlier as "Banjo Betty," the German name is *Gesangsprobe,* or "Singing Rehearsal." It also appears as a candy box and as one of the set of bookends. Sister M.I. Hummel's original drawing is unlocated to date.

III/53 Joyful, *Candy Box, new style box, TMK-5.*

III/53 Joyful, Candy Box

Indicator	Size	Status	TMK-1	TMK-2	TMK-3	TMK-4	TMK-5	TMK-6
III/53	6¼"	D,a	350	250	200	—	—	—
III/53	6¼"	P,b	—	—	130	110	94	85

(a – bowl-shaped bottom. b – bottom with vertical sides.)

This candy box, when first designed and released in the 1930s, was rounded in the form of a semisphere or bowl. The cover was slightly crowned and designed to fit inside and flush with the top edges of the bowl. In the early 1960s the box was redesigned, along with other candy boxes, in a cylindrical shape with vertical sides and a flanged top which was flush with the sides.

54 Silent Night, *Candleholder, trademark unknown.*

54 Silent Night, Candleholder

Indicator	Size	Status	TMK-1	TMK-2	TMK-3	TMK-4	TMK-5	TMK-6
54	3¾"	P,a	350	225	140	120	105	95
54	3¾"	D,b	6,000	4,000	—	—	—	—

(a – all white children. b – one standing child is black.)

This model can be and frequently is confused with Hum. 31. The Hum. 31 black child wears an earring but no shoes; the hair is smooth and less detailed than that of the same white children in Hum. 54. The German name for Hum. 54 is *Stille Nacht, Krippe mit Kerzentülle,"* or "Silent Night, Creche with Candleholder." An event in 1979 futher stimulated questions when a reader reported an example of Hum. 54 with a black child. The incised 54 on the back was verified (see page 170 in *Hummel Art II*). The original drawing is owned by Ars Edition and cataloged as H 624.

55 Saint George

Indicator	Size	Status	TMK-1	TMK-2	TMK-3	TMK-4	TMK-5	TMK-6
55	6¾"	D,a	800	—	—	—	—	—
55	6¾"	P,b	500	250	200	170	150	135

(a – horse has dark red saddle. b – horse has light color saddle.)

This piece is of a representation of the mythical medieval English knight and patron saint of soldiers. The Saint George has also been reported in white overglaze. At least one of these figurines with early trademarks has been reported with a dark red saddle. In addition to "Saint George," Hum. 55 has been called "St. George and the Dragon" and "Knight Saint George" after the German name *Ritter Heiliger Georg.* No lithographic reproduction or original of the drawing has been found to date.

55 Saint George, *TMK-5.*

56/A Culprits

Indicator	Size	Status	TMK-1	TMK-2	TMK-3	TMK-4	TMK-5	TMK-6
56.	6¼"	D,a	400	—	—	—	—	—
56	6¼"	P,a	375	325	—	—	—	—
56/A	6¼"	D,a	350	200	175	—	—	—
56/A	6¼"	P,b	—	—	150	125	110	100

(a – boy's eyes open. b. – boy's eyes closed, looking down.)

This was also introduced in the 1930s and listed in an early 1947 catalog as Apple Thief, Boy, which is also the translation of its German name, *Apfeldieb, Junge.* At that time it was listed for $9 and marked 56 only, indicating the companion Out of Danger was not listed until somewhat later in the 1950s. In these earlier, smoother models, the boy was not looking directly down at the dog as in the later, restyled version. Verlag Emil Fink has published postcard 223 of this motif.

56/A Culprits, *TMK-5.*

56/B Out of Danger

Indicator	Size	Status	TMK-1	TMK-2	TMK-3	TMK-4	TMK-5	TMK-6
56/B	6¼"	D,a	350	200	175	—	—	—
56/B	6¼"	P,b	—	—	150	125	110	100

(a – girl's eyes open. b – girl's eyes closed, looking down.)

This piece is listed in a 1959 catalog for $9. Examples of Hum. 56B made in the 1950s show the girl looking straight ahead (called "eyes open" by collectors). The original name was "Girl in Safety," which is the translation of the present German name, *In Sicherheit, Mädchen.*

56/B Out of Danger, *TMK-5.*

57 Chick Girl

57/0 Chick Girl, *TMK-5.*

Indicator	Size	Status	TMK-1	TMK-2	TMK-3	TMK-4	TMK-5	TMK-6
57	3¼"	D	300	225	—	—	—	—
57.	3½"	D	350	250	—	—	—	—
57/0	3½"	P	250	125	100	80	70	63
57/0	4"	D,a	800	—	—	—	—	—
57.	4¼"	D	450	350	—	—	—	—
57/1	4¼"	P	275	200	150	120	105	95
57/1	4½"	D,a	—	—	1,000	—	—	—

(a – chick missing on base.)

This model, introduced in the 1930s and marked only 57 or 57. (decimal), was listed as 4" high in the 1947 catalog. The larger size has three chicks in the basket instead of two as in the small first version. Presently 57/0 and 57/1 are listed as 3½" and 4¼" high, respectively. It will appear as the motif on the 1985 plate. Its German name, *Kükenmütterchen*, is "Little Chick Mother." The original drawing is owned by Ars Edition, and cataloged as H 371.

III/57 Chick Girl, Candy Box

III/57 Chick Girl, *Candy Box, new style box, TMK-5.*

Indicator	Size	Status	TMK-1	TMK-2	TMK-3	TMK-4	TMK-5	TMK-6
III/57	6¼"	D,a	400	300	200	—	—	—
III/57	6¼"	P,b	—	—	130	110	94	85

(a – bowl-shaped bottom. b – bottom has vertical sides.)

The Roman three (III) prefix is used to indicate that model 57 has been superimposed on a candy box. The early issue was curved in a cup or bowl shape, and the top was inset flush with the sides. In the early 1960s, the box was redesigned. The bottom is now made with vertical sides with the cap-style cover in the same diameter and flush with the sides.

58 Playmates

58/I Playmates, *TMK-3.*

Indicator	Size	Status	TMK-1	TMK-2	TMK-3	TMK-4	TMK-5	TMK-6
58/0	4"	P	250	125	100	80	70	63
58	4"	D	300	225	—	—	—	—
58/I	4¼"	P	275	200	150	120	105	95

A companion piece to Hum. 57, Chick Girl, Playmates was listed in the 1947 catalog at 4" high. One version of Hum. 58 is pictured with the ears of the farthest rabbit on the reader's left erect. The smaller size is styled with the ears more relaxed and separated. This design is used on the Annual Plate for 1986. "Just Friends" was an alternate name used in the 1947 U.S. catalog, and "Rabbit Father" is the same as the German name, *Hasenvater*. The original drawing is owned by Ars Edition from which graphic H 372 is produced.

Key to Symbols: A — Assigned; C — Cancelled; D — Discontinued; O — Open; P — Produced; R — Reissued; (?) Examples Doubtful; (—) Examples Unlikely.

III/58   Playmates, Candy Box

Indicator	Size	Status	TMK-1	TMK-2	TMK-3	TMK-4	TMK-5	TMK-6
III/58	6¼″	D,a	400	250	150	—	—	—
III/58	6¼″	P,b	—	—	130	110	95	85

(a – old-style box. b – new-style box.)

See III/57, Chick Girl, Candy Box, for the story on marking and design changes in the box. So far there has been only one report of this candy box with the Crown mark, TMK-1. On the newer style box, the far right rabbit's ears follow the positioning of the ones in 58/0. Both shapes of boxes have been used on this as mentioned under III/57. The straight-sided cylinder design may have TMK-3 through 6.

III/58 Playmates, *Candy Box, new style box, TMK-5.*

59   Skier

Indicator	Size	Status	TMK-1	TMK-2	TMK-3	TMK-4	TMK-5	TMK-6
59	5″	P	300	200	125	105	95	84
59.	6″	D	500	—	—	—	—	—

Another design from the 1930s, it is listed in the 1947 U.S. catalog as 5½″ high for $7.50. These early models had wooden poles and wooden fiber disks. At an indefinite date, poles were changed to wooden with metal disks, then to metal or plastic poles. Any examples with the oldest trademarks should have original wooden poles. The above prices are only for figurines with poles that are original to the piece. The German name of *Ski-Heil* translates as "Hail, Skiing." The original drawing, owned by Ars Edition, is used for graphic H 315.

59 Skier, *no trademark.*

60 A   Farm Boy,
60 B   Goosegirl, Bookends

Indicator	Size	Status	TMK-1	TMK-2	TMK-3	TMK-4	TMK-5	TMK-6
60 A&B	4¾″	P	600	400	300	250?	230	210

These two Bavarian country children are sold only as a pair. These early-design bookends have the figures mounted directly on the wooden base, whereas the later ones such as Apple Tree Boy and Girl, 252 A and 252 B, have the figurines on the normal integral ceramic base which is mounted and glued to the wooden bookends. For this reason, the trademark is on the wooden base itself, rather than on the figurine. Refer to Goose Girl, Hum. 47, and Farm Boy, Hum. 66, for more history.

60 A&B Farm Boy and Goose Girl, *Bookends, TMK-3.*

61 A&B Playmates and Chick Girl,
Bookends, TMK-3.

61 A   Playmates,
61 B   Chick Girl, Bookends

Indicator	Size	Status	TMK-1	TMK-2	TMK-3	TMK-4	TMK-5	TMK-6
61 A&B	4"	P	600	400	300	280	230	210

Refer to the figurines Hum. 58 and Hum. 57 for further details. Like the preceding pair of Hum. 60 bookends, these figures were also mounted directly on the wooden bases rather than the composite ceramic figurine and base mounted on the wooden platforms. These are trademarked on the back of the wooden base. In the 1950 catalog these also were listed as Hum. 61 only and, therefore, might be found marked that way. By 1965, the catalogs listed them with separate alphabetical letters.

62 Happy Pastime, *Ashtray,*
TMK-3.

62   Happy Pastime, Ashtray

Indicator	Size	Status	TMK-1	TMK-2	TMK-3	TMK-4	TMK-5	TMK-6
62	3½"	P	250	165	115	95	85	75

Sister Hummel's original drawing shows the bird in an adjacent tree, somewhat as it is positioned in the 1978 Annual Plate. First called "Ashtray with Knitter," other names are "Little Knitter," and "Knitting Liesl," the translation of the German name *Stickliesl*. The current models have the signature on the back of the figurine. Refer to Hum. 69, Happy Pastime, for further details.

63 Singing Lesson, *TMK-5.*

63   Singing Lesson

Indicator	Size	Status	TMK-1	TMK-2	TMK-3	TMK-4	TMK-5	TMK-6
63	2¾"	P	180	120	80	70	60	53
63.	2¾"	D	225	—	—	—	—	—

Some of the compromises that had to be made in adapting Sister Hummel's original into three-dimensional figures can be seen by comparing the bas-relief motif on the 1979 Annual Plate, Hum. 272, with the photograph of Singing Lesson, Hum. 63. This introduction in the 1930s was listed in the 1950 catalog as "Duet." Frequently this piece commands a premium at auctions and sales because it is often paired with the 1979 Annual Plate, Hum. 272, for display in shadow boxes. The original drawing is owned by Ars Edition from which they produce graphic H 305.

III/63   Singing Lesson, Candy Box

Indicator	Size	Status	TMK-1	TMK-2	TMK-3	TMK-4	TMK-5	TMK-6
III/63	6″	D,a	400	250	150	—	—	—
III/63	6″	P,b	—	—	130	110	95	85

(a – bottom is bowl-shaped. b – bottom side vertical.)

When the model number is preceded by the Roman three (III), this is an indication that the article is a candy box. See Hum. 63 for more details on the background of this design. As with other boxes, its shape when first introduced in the 1930s was more spherical; the design was changed later in the early 1960s to straight-sided. The positioning of the arms and head may vary in the assembly.

III/63 Singing Lesson, *Candy Box, new style box, TMK-5.*

64   Shepherd's Boy

Indicator	Size	Status	TMK-1	TMK-2	TMK-3	TMK-4	TMK-5	TMK-6
64	5½″	P	275	200	120	110	95	84

When first designed in the 1930s, this figure had somewhat different facial characteristics than the present model which also has brighter colors. This piece differs from Lost Sheep, Hum. 68, by having a second lamb standing in front of the shepherd. In an early catalog, they were both called "Shepherd's Boy" and distinguished by the description of the lambs. (See *Hummel Art II* for the Beswick Hummel in this design.) A photograph in color of Hum. 64 is the month of April for the 1968 calendar. The original drawing belongs to Verlag Emil Fink. A lithograph of this in postcard form is available as 204/A.

64 Shepherd's Boy, *TMK-5.*

65   Farewell

Indicator	Size	Status	TMK-1	TMK-2	TMK-3	TMK-4	TMK-5	TMK-6
65/0	4″	D	2,500	—	—	—	—	—
65/I	4½″	D	300	250	200	175	135	—
65.	4¾″	D	450	350	—	—	—	—
65	4¾″	P	—	—	—	—	115	105

Currently cataloged as number 65 (only), 4¾″ high, Farewell was also listed in earlier catalogs as 65 (only), but later appeared as 65/0 for a short time with only a few examples known. Examples were also cataloged as large as 5½″ high and marked either 65 or 65/I in the 1950s. The ones marked 65/I have been reported in TMK-3 and in later marks. Such examples would carry a premium of about 15 percent over the same height marked 65 (only). The figurine was also called "Goodbye" and "Till We Meet Again." The original drawing is owned by Ars Edition, who has produced graphic H 310.

65 Farewell, *TMK-5.*

66 Farm Boy, *TMK-3.*

66 Farm Boy

Indicator	Size	Status	TMK-1	TMK-2	TMK-3	TMK-4	TMK-5	TMK-6
66.	5″	D	300	200	150	125	100	—
66	5″	P	—	—	—	—	90	84

This piece has had a variety of names since first introduced in the 1930s. A 1947 catalog lists it as "Pig Boy," while a 1950 one called it "Three Pals." The German name *Schweinehirt* translates, obviously, as "Swineherd." While it has only been made in one size, about 5″ high, examples as late as TMK-5 have been reported as being marked 66. (decimal). The 1947 catalog listed this as 5½″ high and the price was $8. The location of the original drawing is unknown at present.

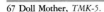

67 Doll Mother, *TMK-5.*

67 Doll Mother

Indicator	Size	Status	TMK-1	TMK-2	TMK-3	TMK-4	TMK-5	TMK-6
67.	4¼″	D	400	300	—	—	—	—
67	4¾″	P	300	200	160	120	100	90

Originally called "Little Doll Mother" and listed in the early catalogs as being only 4¼″ high, this model is currently about 4¾″ high. It was restyled some time ago and modifications were apparently minor but in line with the brighter palette and textured finish typical of Skrobek. A popular collector's item, with old marks it frequently sells at premium prices at auctions and sales. The original drawing is owned by Ars Edition, from which graphic H 164 is currently available.

68/0 Lost Sheep, *TMK-5.*

68 Lost Sheep

Indicator	Size	Status	TMK-1	TMK-2	TMK-3	TMK-4	TMK-5	TMK-6
68/2/0	4¼″	P,b	—	120	85	70	60	53
68.	5¼″	D,b	300	250	—	—	—	—
68.	5¼″	D,a	350	300	—	—	—	—
68	5¼″	D,a	325	275	—	—	—	—
68	5¼″	D,b	300	250	—	—	—	—
68/0	5½″	P,b	—	180	110	90	80	74

(a – brown pants. b – green pants.)

This model is similar to Shepherd's Boy, Hum. 64, except that it has a single lamb and the colors of the jacket and pants are different. It was once called "Shepherd's Boy," which is its German name, *Schäferbub.* A new U.S. Copyright, GF98, on January 1, 1963, used the name "Lost Sheep." This figurine adorns the April page of the 1968 calendar. The original drawing for the figurine, Shepherd's Boy, Hum. 64, is also thought to have been the inspiration for Lost Sheep, Hum. 68.

69   Happy Pastime

Indicator	Size	Status	TMK-1	TMK-2	TMK-3	TMK-4	TMK-5	TMK-6
69.	3½″	D	275	200	—	—	—	—
69	3½″	P	250	200	100	85	70	63

By referring to the picture of the 1978 Annual Plate, Hum. 271, one has an idea of how Sister Hummel's original drawing appeared. In the figurine, the bird was placed at the side of the busy knitter instead of in a tree. The only major change is in the name, from "Knitter" to "Happy Pastime," sometime after 1950. No major variations in design or coloring have been reported to date. The original drawing is owned by Ars Edition and graphics from it are available from them as number H 306.

69 Happy Pastime, *TMK-5.*

III/69   Happy Pastime, Candy Box

Indicator	Size	Status	TMK-1	TMK-2	TMK-3	TMK-4	TMK-5	TMK-6
III/69	6½″	D,a	400	300	150	—	—	—
III/69	6½″	P,b	—	—	130	110	94	95
III/69	6½″	D,c	600	500	—	—	—	—

(a – bottom is bowl-shaped. b – bottom has straight side. c – green trim around box.)

Refer to Hum. 69 for design notes on the figure. The candy box shape was redesigned in the mid-1960s. (See note on Joyful, III/53, for more details.) One interesting variation of this candy box, found with a pastel green rim on both the bottom and top of the old-style box, commands a premium over the plain version. The original drawing was the same one used for the 1978 Annual Plate, Hum. 271, and the figurine, Hum. 69.

III/69 Happy Pastime, *Candy Box, new style box, TMK-5.*

70   The Holy Child

Indicator	Size	Status	TMK-1	TMK-2	TMK-3	TMK-4	TMK-5	TMK-6
70	6¾″	P	250	150	100	80?	70	60

This illustrates Sister Hummel's ability to depict serenity and piety in her religious drawings. Probably issued in the late 1930s, the later catalogs show a wide range of sizes for the same model number. Those over 7″ high should bring a premium of 10 to 20 percent. In a ten-year span they ranged from 6¾″ to 7½″ high. The later trademarks have the typical restyling characteristic of master modeler Gerhard Skrobek. The only other name recorded is the English translation of *Jeswein,* "Little Jesus." The location of the original drawing by Sister Hummel has not been determined. No graphics published from the original were found.

70 The Holy Child, *TMK-3.*

71 Stormy Weather, *TMK-5.*

71   Stormy Weather

Indicator	Size	Status	TMK-1	TMK-2	TMK-3	TMK-4	TMK-5	TMK-6
71	6¼"	P	550	400	300	220?	205	190
71.	6½"	D	650	—	—	—	—	—

This figurine's appeal was broadened even more with the use of its motif in bas-relief for the First Anniversary Plate, Hum. 280, in 1975. The figurine portrays awe and fear on the children's faces, while the plate shows them with radiant smiles. Sister Hummel did two similar drawings for Ars Edition, who published two graphics H 288 and H 287. These have been referred to as "Stormy Weather" and "Sunny Weather," respectively, indicating the reason for the change in mood. In the 1950s this piece was cataloged as "Under the Roof," which agrees with the German name *Unter einem Dach.* Actual pieces range from about 6¼" to 7 " high.

72 Spring Cheer, *TMK-3.*

72   Spring Cheer

Indicator	Size	Status	TMK-1	TMK-2	TMK-3	TMK-4	TMK-5	TMK-6
72	5"	D,a	250	175	125	—	—	—
72	5"	P,b	—	—	90	70	60	53
72	5"	D,c	—	—	1,000+	—	—	—

(*a – yellow dress, no flowers.* *b – green dress, flowers in right hand.* *c – green dress, no flowers in right hand.*)

Another adaptation before World War II and at that time called, "It's Spring," which corresponds to the present German name, *Fruhling ist's.* In the May 1980 calendar, this figurine is well illustrated in a naturalized background. The original drawing at Ars Edition is used by them to publish H 271.

73 Little Helper, *TMK-3.*

73   Little Helper

Indicator	Size	Status	TMK-1	TMK-2	TMK-3	TMK-4	TMK-5	TMK-6
73.	4¼"	D	250	200	—	—	—	—
73	4¼"	P	200	120	70	65	60	53

One source indicates this has been in production from the mid-1930s. In a 1955 catalog it was called "Diligent Betsy," but changed to the above name before 1959. The German name indicates that this is referred to as "Busy Little Liesl" or *Fleissiges Lieschen.* It is interesting to note that the basket, which has been empty for many years, is to be filled in the 1984 Plate version. The original drawing was used by Ars Edition to produce graphic H 340.

74 Little Gardener

Indicator	Size	Status	TMK-1	TMK-2	TMK-3	TMK-4	TMK-5	TMK-6
74.	4"	D,a	240	200	—	—	—	—
74	4"	D,a	200	150	100	—	—	—
74	4"	P,b	—	—	75	65	60	53

(a − raised flower, oval base. b − round base.)

74 **Little Gardener,** *round base,*
TMK-3.

This figurine has had the same name in German *(Die kleine Gärtnerin)* and in English for over forty years. However, the color of the smock background has varied from the yellow side to the chartreuse side and the dots on it have been more accentuated in some cases. In the 1960s the base was changed from oval to round. The round-base features a flatter flower. Colored pictures of the later version appear in the calendars for May 1969 and July 1978. No original drawing or published graphic was found for this motif.

75 Angelic Prayer (White Angel), Holy Water Font

Indicator	Size	Status	TMK-1	TMK-2	TMK-3	TMK-4	TMK-5	TMK-6
75	3¼"	P	75	50	30	25	20	17

75 **Angelic Prayer,** *Holy Water Font,*
new style with hole at top, TMK-3.

Confusion exists concerning the appropriate name (both are listed in the Alphabetical Index). The German name, *Weisser Engel,* translates as "White Angel" which is still used in Germany and in some publications. The 1980 catalogs for two of the U.S. distributors list Hum. 75 as "Angelic Prayer" which is in line with some other early catalogs. When it was restyled, possibly in the 1960s by Skrobek, a hole was added at the top for hanging. Previously, a concealed hole was provided on the back. The location of the original drawing used for this adaptation is not known at present.

76A Doll Mother,
76B Prayer Before Battle, Bookends

Indicator	Size	Status	TMK-1	TMK-2	TMK-3	TMK-4	TMK-5	TMK-6
76A&B	4¾"	*	—	—	—	—	—	—

76 A **Doll Mother,** *Bookend, c.*
1937, TMK-1. Factory prototype courtesy
of W. Goebel Co.

Illustrated for the first time in print through the courtesy of the Goebel Collectors' Club Museum in Tarrytown, New York, is 76 A, Doll Mother, half of this set of bookends. Factory records indicate that Doll Mother was not produced after 1938 and any other examples of either one would be a rare find, probably valued in the very high four-digit figures. The trademark and other identification are on the wooden base.
*Factory sample of 76 A only, pair if found valued in low five digits.

77 Cross with Doves, Holy Water Font (CN)

Indicator	Size	Status	TMK-1	TMK-2	TMK-3	TMK-4	TMK-5	TMK-6
77	6¼"	C	10,000	—	—	—	—	—

Originally this number was listed by the factory as a sample model that was never released for sale. A surprising discovery by one of our readers who sent the accompanying picture for verification occurred in 1979. As far as is known, this is the only exception to the sample that is maintained in the factory archives. The German name is *Kreuz mit Tauben*, the same as the English translation. The original drawing does not appear to have been published in graphic form and its location has not been determined.

77 **Cross with Doves,** *Holy Water Font, only example known, TMK-1.* Photograph by Cheryl Trotter.

78/111 Infant of Krumbad, *TMK-5.*

78 Infant of Krumbad

Indicator	Size	Status	TMK-1	TMK-2	TMK-3	TMK-4	TMK-5	TMK-6
78/0	2"	D	—	150	100	—	—	—
78/I (US)	2½"	P	125	100	40	30	25	20
78/II (US)	3½"	P	140	120	45	35	30	25
78/III (US)	4½"	P	160	140	50	45	35	30
78/V	7¾"	P	200	160	75	65	50	40
78/VI	11"	P	300	175	100	80	70	60
78/VIII	13½"	P	400	250	175	150	125	100

The figurine is a replica of the only known sculpture to have been done by the hands of Sister Hummel. There are three completed studies of this which are displayed in the public museum in the Franciscan Convent in Siessen, Germany. These were executed in papier-maché and have a twisted wire halo that is secured in two holes on the back. Only three sizes are currently available from U.S. distributors in the lightly tinted beige bisque. It may be found in other sizes and finishes in Germany. A 1950 catalog called it "In the Crib." It has been produced in white bisque and also in full color in Germany. One authority suggests that a mold change occurred in the Full Bee time period; the U.S. Copyright GF375 says July 7, 1966; another source has reported a regular incised Crown plus an unknown stamped Crown with a "roof mark," similar to a "V" inverted. For more information on this mark variation, see *Hummel Art II*. More research is required to fully document when, where, in what sizes and colors these were made. Ars Edition has published graphic H 474 of the original drawing.

79 Globe Trotter

Indicator	Size	Status	TMK-1	TMK-2	TMK-3	TMK-4	TMK-5	TMK-6
79	5"	D,a	300	225	125	—	—	—
79	5"	P,b	—	—	100	85	76	69

(a – double-strand weave in basket. b – single-strand weave.)

"Out into the Distance" is a translation of the German name, *Hinaus in die Ferne.* It has been made with two distinctive styles of woven basket. The older version is woven with a double parallel strand using an over-and-under crisscross weave. The newer version has a basket of the same weave but executed in single strands. The price differentials are included above. Each design is found in TMK-3 and 4. It was used as a bas-relief design on the plate of 1973, Hum. 266 (note differences in treatment). The original drawing is owned by Ars Edition, who has published it as graphic H 216.

79 **Globe Trotter,** *single weave basket, TMK-5.*

80 Little Scholar

Indicator	Size	Status	TMK-1	TMK-2	TMK-3	TMK-4	TMK-5	TMK-6
80	5½"	P	225	175	110	85	76	69

When this piece was restyled at an undetermined date (possibly the 1960s), the shoe color was changed from brown to a grayish black. The German name of *Erster Schulgang, Junge* means "Boy's First Trip to School," similar to Hum. 81. These two were probably planned as a pair. The nonchalant "School Boy Truant," Hum. 82, became "School Boy" and was paired with School Girl, Hum. 81. The original drawing is owned by Ars Edition, who has published a replica as graphic H 192.

80 Little Scholar, *TMK-5.*

81 School Girl

Indicator	Size	Status	TMK-1	TMK-2	TMK-3	TMK-4	TMK-5	TMK-6
81/2/0	4¼"	P	200	140	85	70	60	53
81/0	5"	P	225	160	100	90	80	69
81.	5½"	D	280	225	—	—	—	—
81	5½"	D	250	—	—	—	—	—

In 1956 it was called "Little Scholar." While the school girl's basket is empty in the 81 and 81/0 marks, the basket is full in the smaller sized 81/2/0. The Annual Plate for 1980, Hum. 273, enhances the demand for this popular figurine. Note that the 1980 Annual Plate reveals the basket with knitting in it. The original drawing is owned by Ars Edition, who has published graphic H 191 from it.

Mar Christmas '86

81/2/0 School Girl, *TMK-3.*

82 School Boy

Indicator	Size	Status	TMK-1	TMK-2	TMK-3	TMK-4	TMK-5	TMK-6
82/2/0	4″	P	150	125	75	65	60	53
82/0	5″	P	220	150	100	85	75	69
82.	5½″	D	300	250	100	—	—	—
82/II(2)	7¾″	R	600	500	400	—	205	185

Although the German name *Schulschwänzer, Junge* is still in use today, by 1947 "Schoolboy Truant" had changed to "School Boy" and was listed in one size only, 5½″ high. The large size had been dropped by 1966. This large size remained out of production and was considered rare until it was reintroduced in limited quantities overseas in 1978. No significant changes in design or color have been recorded over the years. The original drawing's location has not been ascertained and no graphics were located.

82/2/0 School Boy, *TMK-3.*

83 Angel Serenade

Indicator	Size	Status	TMK-1	TMK-2	TMK-3	TMK-4	TMK-5	TMK-6
83	5½″	R	450	350	250	150?	90	80

This has been in the line since the 1930s, and in the 1960s, it was no longer available in the U.S. Thus it became a high-priced rarity until 1978 when it was reintroduced in the same 5½″ size at a fraction of the price old marks were commanding. It is too early to tell what will happen to the prices for the old marks. Originally called "Pious Melodies," or "Devout Tunes" after the German *Fromme Weisen.* The original drawing has not been located at this time, nor are there any graphics.

83 Angel Serenade, *rare. TMK-3. Reissued.*

84 Worship

Indicator	Size	Status	TMK-1	TMK-2	TMK-3	TMK-4	TMK-5	TMK-6
84/0	5″	P	275	160	100	80	75	65
84.	5¼″	D	350	—	—	—	—	—
84/V(5)	12¾″	R	1,800	1,400	800	750?	650	600

This model was first called "At the Wayside," after the German name, *Am Wegesrand, Bildstökl,* in the 1930s. It is more recently cataloged as 84/0; the large size 84/V has been reported marked 84/5 (arabic). One of the smaller sizes has been found in white glaze and valued in the low four-digit figures. The original drawing is owned by Ars Edition, who used it to publish graphic H 280. Hum.84/V was reintroduced in the U.S. in 1978.

84/0 Worship, *TMK-5.*

Key to Symbols: A — Assigned; C — Cancelled; D — Discontinued; O — Open; P — Produced; R — Reissued; (?) Examples Doubtful; (—) Examples Unlikely.

85 Serenade

Indicator	Size	Status	TMK-1	TMK-2	TMK-3	TMK-4	TMK-5	TMK-6
85/0	4¾"	P,b	200	125	75	65	60	53
85/0	5"	D,a	250	150	85	75	—	—
85.	7¼"	D,a	800	450	—	—	—	—
85/II(2)	7½"	P,a	700	350	250	225	205	185

(a – fingers up. b – fingers down.)

The fingers of the "Flutist" (an early name) are found either up or down. Some very old models have two fingers extended; some of the newer ones do, too. This figurine is sometimes used in assembling a Hummel orchestra of musicians and singers, which makes quite an impressive grouping. "Boy Serenading with Flute" is the translation of the German, *Ständchen, Junge mit Flöte*. The original drawing is owned by Ars Edition who used it to publish graphic H 342.

85/0 Serenade, *TMK-3.*

86 Happiness

Indicator	Size	Status	TMK-1	TMK-2	TMK-3	TMK-4	TMK-5	TMK-6
86	4¾"	P	200	140	75	65?	58	53

First called "Wandersong" after the German name, *Wanderlied, Mädchen* ("Hiking Girl Song"). This happy, hiking girl, strumming a banjo as she strolls, is a particularly appealing example of the carefree innocence and joy which Sister Hummel conveyed so dramatically in her art. The original drawing from which this was adapted with some artistic license depicted two girls striding in step, the far girl carrying a staff and the closest one as shown here with a banjo. This has been published as graphic H 274 by Ars Edition, who owns the original.

86 Happiness, *TMK-3.*

87 For Father

Indicator	Size	Status	TMK-1	TMK-2	TMK-3	TMK-4	TMK-5	TMK-6
87.	5"	D,b	350	325	—	—	—	—
87	5½"	D,a	1,000	800	600	—	—	—
87	5½"	P,b	300	200	150	100	90	80

(a – red-orange radish. b – light tan radish.)

Sometime before 1950 this figurine was called Father's Joy. It is found in all trademarks ranging from 5" to 5½" high. The German translation is "For the Little Father, Radish Boy" from *Fürs Vaterle, Rettichbub*. It is one of the popular models and makes a nice companion piece with the figurine For Mother, Hum. 257. The original drawing is owned by Ars Edition who used it to produce graphic H 302.

87 For Father, *TMK-2.*

88 Heavenly Protection

Indicator	Size	Status	TMK-1	TMK-2	TMK-3	TMK-4	TMK-5	TMK-6
88	9¼"	D	—	700	500	—	—	—
88.	9¼"	D	1,000	800	600	—	—	—
88/I	6¾"	P	—	—	215	185	165	147
88/II	9"	P	—	500	400	275?	245	220

Early pieces are found incised with either model number 88 (only) or 88/II, both around 9" high. The smaller size, 88/I, is listed TMK-3. The two children appear to have been modeled from Hum. 94, Surprise, and combined with one of the numerous protective angels drawn by Sister Hummel, since no composite drawing or graphic was located resembling the figurine. One surprisingly good reproduction made years ago in Japan is almost identical. Of course, it does not have the M.J.Hummel facsimile signature incised on it.

88/I Heavenly Protection, *TMK-5.*

89 Little Cellist

Indicator	Size	Status	TMK-1	TMK-2	TMK-3	TMK-4	TMK-5	TMK-6
89./I(1)	5¾"	D,a	375	350	—	—	—	—
89/1	6¼"	D,a	350	225	150	—	—	—
89(.)	7½"	D,b	850	—	—	—	—	—
89/I	6¼"	P,b	—	—	120	100?	90	84
89/II	7½"	P,b	700	350	250	225?	200	185

(a – eyes open, looking ahead. b – eyes closed, looking down.)

Early catalogs list 89/I at 5¾". The larger size, 89/II, was introduced sometime in the 1950s and is about 7½" high. A distinct variation exists in this motif. At first the Little Cellist looked directly at the viewer as he plodded along. In the newer style he is paying more attention to where he is going by looking down. The base of the newer example has rounded or chamfered corners. The original drawing is owned by Ars Edition who has produced graphic H 250 from it.

89/I Little Cellist, *eyes down, TMK-5.*

90 Cancelled Number

Indicator	Size	Status	TMK-1	TMK-2	TMK-3	TMK-4	TMK-5	TMK-6
90 A&B	?	C	*	—	—	—	—	—

Here is a challenge to dedicated flea "marketeers" and possessors of "atticana." Research by Robert Miller and the Goebel Company has established that this number was assigned to a pair of bookends using the figurine Eventide, Hum. 99, and Adoration, Hum. 23 without the shrine, for design and prototypes for possible production. Both figures are mounted directly on the wooden base as were other early models. According to these records all work was discontinued in February 1939, and only a factory sample is now known to exist. Any prototype or early model would be marked TMK-1. While it is extremely unlikely that other than a factory sample exists, such an authenticated example would have an insurable value in the five-digit figures.
*Factory sample only.

91 A&B Angels at Prayer, Holy Water Fonts

Indicator	Size	Status	TMK-1	TMK-2	TMK-3	TMK-4	TMK-5	TMK-6
91 (.)	4½"	D,a	200	—	—	—	—	—
91 A&B	4¾"	D,a	160	100	60	—	—	—
91 A&B	4¾"	P,b	—	—	—	44	40	33

(a – no halos. b – with halos.)

91 A&B Angels at Prayer, *Holy Water Fonts, with haloes and holes, TMK-5.*

Angel at Prayer (facing left) is reported incised with 91 only. They are found with all trademarks indicating a good long production pattern. It appears that the model facing left was introduced first as one model with Crown mark incised and 91 (only). The one facing right was introduced later. They are presently listed as a pair. Sometime in the 1960s, they were redesigned (as shown in the photograph) by adding the halo background and piercing a hole above the head for hanging. The prices above reflect this change.

92 Merry Wanderer, Plaque

Indicator	Size	Status	TMK-1	TMK-2	TMK-3	TMK-4	TMK-5	TMK-6
92.	5"x5½"	D	300	—	—	—	—	—
92	5"x5½"	D	250	150	—	—	—	—
92	4¾"x5"	P	—	—	100	85	75	65

92 Merry Wanderer, *Plaque, TMK-5.*

Two U.S. copyrights, December 31, 1938, and December 15, 1968, indicate important dates that approximate introduction and revision. This plaque is known in all trademarks, and examples as large as 5" x 5½" with Crown marks have been reported. The prices allow a premium for the larger pieces. If the plaque is signed on *both* the front and back with , add 15 percent premium. The German name, *Bild, Wanderhub,* translates as "Wanderer Boy." This is the same motif as used in the figurines Merry Wanderer, Hum. 7 and Hum. 11 (see these models for more details).

93 Little Fiddler, Plaque

Indicator	Size	Status	TMK-1	TMK-2	TMK-3	TMK-4	TMK-5	TMK-6
93	5"x5½"	D,a	2,000	—	—	—	—	—
93	5"x5½"	P,b	250	150	—	—	—	—
93	4½"x5"	P,b	—	—	100	85	75	65

(a – old style, 3 houses. b – new style, 6 houses.)

93 Little Fiddler, *Plaque, TMK-5.*

This apparently was designed as a companion piece to Hum. 92. It was registered in the U.S. Copyright Office on December 31, 1939, but not widely distributed in the U.S. This plaque is intriguing because it was issued with two different backgrounds. The earlier design had only three houses. The present design was probably covered by U.S. Copyright on February 23, 1968, and shows six houses. The Hum. 107 is even rarer at this time and can be distinguished by the wooden frame.

94/I Surprise, *TMK-2.*

94 Surprise

Indicator	Size	Status	TMK-1	TMK-2	TMK-3	TMK-4	TMK-5	TMK-6
94/3/0	4″	P,a	—	140	100	—	70	63
94/2/0	4½″	D,a	—	—	2,000	—	—	—
94(.)	5¾″	D,a	400	300	—	—	—	—
94/I	5½″	P,a	350	250	175	—	—	—
94/I	5½″	P,b	—	—	130	115	100	90

(a – rectangular or chamfered corners. b – round base.)

This model has three names, "Surprise," "The Duet," and "Hansel and Gretel," the English translation of the German name, *Hänsel and Gretl.* In addition to the ones shown above, there is a figurine with the 94. (decimal) incised over a previously incised number 82 in one case, and number 38 in a similar case. Both of these carry the Full Bee trademark in TMK-2. Older marks used either a rectangular base or a base with chamfered corners. Almost all later models are made with an oval base. Major deviations like the doubled over stamp might be valued in the high hundreds.

95 Brother, *TMK-3.*

95 Brother

Indicator	Size	Status	TMK-1	TMK-2	TMK-3	TMK-4	TMK-5	TMK-6
95.		D,a	300	200	—	—	—	—
95	4¾″	P,b	250	160	100	80?	70	63

(a – light blue jacket. b – dark blue jacket.)

While this piece was never called "Hansel," it appears to be identical to the boy of that German name in Hum. 94. Hum. 95's German name, *Dorfheld,* translates as "Village Hero." Examples over 5″ high would merit a premium of 10 percent or more. The location of the original drawing is unknown at present with the possibility that this may have been based on a figure that was part of a composite group. Variations in suspenders may be found.

96 Little Shopper, *TMK-5.*

96 Little Shopper

Indicator	Size	Status	TMK-1	TMK-2	TMK-3	TMK-4	TMK-5	TMK-6
96	5½″	P	180	120	90	65?	60	53

If number 95 is "Hansel," then Hum. 96 must be the "Gretel" in the figurine, Surprise, Hum. 94. This is verified by the German name which reads the same. Any found more than 6″ high would be worth 10 percent more. In the early catalogs this piece was called "Errand Girl." Some minor color variations have been reported which are to be expected with many different artists doing the decorating. There does not seem to be a separate drawing of "Gretel" or any graphics published from it.

97 Trumpet Boy

Indicator	Size	Status	TMK-1	TMK-2	TMK-3	TMK-4	TMK-5	TMK-6
97	4¾"	P	225	120	80	70	65	52

This figurine has always been incised with only the model number 97 on the back and no size indicators. However, an analysis of seven different catalogs would make one think otherwise, as the specified sizes range from 4½" high to 5½" high in some of the older models. This piece is called *Der kleine Musikant,* or "The Little Musician." No major variations in color or design have been reported. The location of the original drawing has not been documented, and no graphics copied from such have been found.

97 Trumpet Boy, *TMK-3.*

98 Sister

Indicator	Size	Status	TMK-1	TMK-2	TMK-3	TMK-4	TMK-5	TMK-6
98/2/0	4¾"	P	—	—	80	70	65	53
98/0	5½"	P	—	—	90	80	70	63
98.	5¾"	D	250	175	150	—	—	—
98	5¾"	D,a	5,000	—	—	—	—	—

(a – a prototype with pocketbook, no record of production.)

When Hum. 96 was called "Errand Girl," about 1950, Hum. 98 was known as "Little Shopper." In 1982 a collector reported this made with a pocketbook instead of a basket. This has been verified by the factory as a rare study prototype. Some have been reported with a 1962 copyright date indicating a renewal, which was also recorded as GF96 in the U.S. Copyright Office on January 4, 1963. This motif appears to be the same as the girl in To Market, Hum. 49. The original drawing has not been located to date, nor are there any graphics.

98/0 Sister, *TMK-3.*

99 Eventide

Indicator	Size	Status	TMK-1	TMK-2	TMK-3	TMK-4	TMK-5	TMK-6
99.	4¾"	D	400	325	—	—	—	—
99	4¾"	P	350	300	175	150	135	120
99	4¾"	D,a	—	2,500	—	—	—	—

(a – example of rare white overglaze.)

See Wayside Devotion, Hum. 28, from which this figurine was apparently created by eliminating the shrine. In a 1947 catalog, Hum. 28 was called "Evening Song," the translation of the German name, *Abendlied.* In older models, the girl appears to be looking up at the shrine, rather than straight ahead as in the newer trademarks, which would indicate some restyling. Sister Hummel's original drawing, which includes the omitted shrine, is owned by Ars Edition, who has reproduced it in graphic H 383.

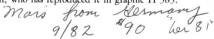

99 Eventide, *TMK-5.*

100 Shrine, Table Lamp

Indicator	Size	Status	TMK-1	TMK-2	TMK-3	TMK-4	TMK-5	TMK-6
100	7½"	D	5,000	4,000?	—	—	—	—

This lamp is a modification of the figurine, Adoration, Hum. 23, substituting the lamp column for the upright post to which the shrine and wreath are attached. Hum. 100 is listed in the Goebel records as a Closed Edition (CE), so very few examples have been located. Two verified examples have TMK-1, and one unverified lamp has both TMK-1 and TMK-2. When found and verified with a Crown and Full Bee marks, this rare piece would be valued as above. The original drawing of the roadside shrine from which this table lamp was adapted is owned by Verlag Emil Fink, who published postcard 839 and prints 100A and 100G as exact replicas of the original drawing.

100 Shrine, *Table Lamp, rare, TMK-1. Grande Collection.*

101 To Market, Table Lamp

Indicator	Size	Status	TMK-1	TMK-2	TMK-3	TMK-4	TMK-5	TMK-6
101	7½"	D,a	5,000	—	—	—	—	—
101	7½"	D,b	—	—	1,500	—	—	—

(a – white column and base. b – tree trunk base.)

This 7½" lamp was created by using the figurine To Market, Hum. 49, on a larger base for stability and by adding a formal white column for the lamp. One Australian collector reported an example with a Full Bee trademark, and another report has been verified with a Stylized Bee (TMK-3) mark. Some years ago the model was redesigned as Hum. 223 and is currently cataloged in the 9½" size only. No U.S. copyright was found.

101 To Market, *Table Lamp, rare, superseded by Hum. 223, TMK-1. Grande Collection.*

102 Volunteers, Table Lamp

Indicator	Size	Status	TMK-1	TMK-2	TMK-3	TMK-4	TMK-5	TMK-6
102	7½"	D	7,500	—	—	—	—	—

One example of this rare lamp exists today in the collection of Robert Miller. Hum. 102 was discontinued in 1937, as were Hummel lamps 101 and 103. Until recently, no known examples existed, not even a factory sample. According to Mr. Miller, the lamp was purchased by a dealer for $14 at a thrift shop in Seattle, Washington. Upon verification of the lamp's markings, Mr. Miller purchased this rare piece valued in the four-digit range. The lamp is marked with an incised number 102, a Double Crown (incised and stamped), a black stamped Germany, and an artist's mark. Hum. 50, the figurine Volunteers, is quite similar in design to the figurine on the lamp 102.

102 Volunteers, *Table Lamp, unique, TMK-1. Miller Collection.*

103   Farewell, Table Lamp

Indicator	Size	Status	TMK-1	TMK-2	TMK-3	TMK-4	TMK-5	TMK-6
103	7½″	C	7,500	—	—	—	—	—

The factory records show this lamp as being a Closed Edition at the same time as the two before, April 1937. An example of this very rare lamp has been exhibited at the Eaton Festival. Another pair exists in the state of Washington.

103 Farewell, Table Lamp, *rare, TMK-1, private collection.*

104   Wayside Devotion, Table Lamp

Indicator	Size	Status	TMK-1	TMK-2	TMK-3	TMK-4	TMK-5	TMK-6
104	?	C	7,500	—	—	—	—	—

This is the fourth lamp in a row that is listed as a Closed Edition by the Goebel Company. This one was discontinued in 1938, an example only recently was added to the Robert Miller collection. Presumably, the post for the shrine in Hum. 28 was replaced by a circular column as in Hum. 100, or a column resembling a tree trunk as used in current models. If a reader is fortunate enough to find one, send us a letter with a good color photograph of the lamp and also one of the base showing all the marks on the bottom.

105   Adoration with Bird

Indicator	Size	Status	TMK-1	TMK-2	TMK-3	TMK-4	TMK-5	TMK-6
105	4¾″	D	8,000	—	—	—	—	—

The first examples of this figurine, which has also been referred to as Bird Lovers, were only recently found and are considered extremely rare. Further research of the factory records indicates that this piece was classified as a Closed Edition in 1938, so it is unlikely that many examples will be discovered. If so, one would be valued in the four-digit range. By observing Hum. 23, Adoration, the adaptation is quite apparent. The shrine that the children gaze at is replaced by a tree trunk with a bird holding the attention of the children. There is no original drawing in this form done by Sister Hummel.

105 Adoration with Bird, *very rare. TMK-1.*

106 Merry Wanderer, *Plaque, artist's concept.*

106 Merry Wanderer, Plaque

Indicator	Size	Status	TMK-1	TMK-2	TMK-3	TMK-4	TMK-5	TMK-6
106	6″	D	8,000	—	—	—	—	—

This piece is identical to Hum. 92 of the same name, with one important exception. This version is only a flat, bas-relief, tilelike piece which has been mounted in a wooden frame. Hum. 92 was molded with an integral, one-piece ceramic frame. This plaque is a Closed Edition, and it is not expected that any more will be made in this style. Since the all-ceramic lookalike, Hum. 92, Merry Wanderer, is still in production, a close inspection will reveal the difference in the frames of ceramic and wood, respectively. This plaque illustrates what Sister Hummel's original drawing looked like with all the background detail in place. (See Hum. 107.) Prints and cards of the original drawing are available from Verlag Emil Fink as 202 and 101A.

107 Little Fiddler, *Plaque, with wooden frame, unique. TMK-1.*

107 Little Fiddler, Plaque

Indicator	Size	Status	TMK-1	TMK-2	TMK-3	TMK-4	TMK-5	TMK-6
107	6″	D	8,000	—	—	—	—	—

This plaque appears to have been made as a companion piece to Hum. 106. This version of the Little Fiddler has the same construction as its companion, being a flat, rectangular, ceramic bas-relief mounted in a wooden frame with a zigzag cloth backing. The first piece to be recorded was discovered in 1978. It is now in the Robert Miller collection. This plaque appears almost identical to a scarce and early version of Hum. 93, Little Fiddler, which has an integrally molded ceramic frame. Another later version of Hum. 93 has a slightly different background, with peaks of six houses rather than three. Prints and cards produced from the original drawing are available from Verlag Emil Fink.

108 Cancelled Number

Indicator	Size	Status	TMK-1	TMK-2	TMK-3	TMK-4	TMK-5	TMK-6
108	?	C	—	—	—	—	—	—

This is another example classified by the company as a closed, or cancelled, number (CN), meaning that it will not be used again. The records indicate that the design was a plaque with an angel and two children. At present there are no known examples, not even a factory sample. Since others in this CN category have surfaced, there is always the remote possibility that at least one or more Hum. 108 will be found somewhere, sometime, by somebody — perhaps you. If you do find one, you should have something equivalent in value to a new small car — no, not a Mercedes.

109   Happy Traveller

Indicator	Size	Status	TMK-1	TMK-2	TMK-3	TMK-4	TMK-5	TMK-6
109.	5″	D	600	—	—	—	—	—
109/0	5″	D	—	125	100	75	65?	?
109	5″	P	—	—	—	—	65	53
109/II(2)	7½″	D,a	—	325	275	235	205	185

(a – in the spring of 1982 Goebel announced that Hum. 109/II was discontinued.)

109 Happy Traveller, *TMK-5.*

Old records going back to 1947 indicate this model has been made in the two sizes, about 5″ and 7½″ high, with minor variations. There is no record to date of any example marked 109/I, which would probably be about 6″ high. Although cataloged earlier as 109/0, current examples are now marked only 109 without any size indicator. The German name, *Hinaus in die Ferne,* translates as "Out in Far Places." The original with the basket has been reproduced as graphic H 216 by Ars Edition.

110   Let's Sing

Indicator	Size	Status	TMK-1	TMK-2	TMK-3	TMK-4	TMK-5	TMK-6
110/0	3″	P	250	150	70	60	55	48
110	4″	D	—	225	—	—	—	—
110.	4″	D	300	—	—	—	—	—
110/I	4″	P	—	200	125	90	75	69

110/0 Let's Sing, *TMK-5.*

The sizes cataloged and found have varied from the standards shown above. One variation reported was an example with feet apart. No other names were found except the German *Heini, Bandoneonspieler,* for "Heini, the Accordion Player." This design was registered on March 31, 1939, and again on February 23, 1967. This motif is also found as the Candy Box listed later; Ashtray, Hum. 114; and as a Closed Edition of Bookends, 120 B, copyrighted before 1940. Ars Edition owns a very similar original, and graphic H 167 is produced from that version.

III/110   Let's Sing, Candy Box

Indicator	Size	Status	TMK-1	TMK-2	TMK-3	TMK-4	TMK-5	TMK-6
III/110	6″	D,a	450?	300	200	—	—	—
III/110	6″	P,b	—	—	130	110	94	85

(a – bowl-shaped bottom. b – bottom has vertical sides.)

III/110 Let's Sing, *Candy Box, new style, TMK-5.*

The Roman numeral III used as a prefix before the model number indicates that the article is a candy box. When first introduced before World War II, the shape of the base was spherical like a deep soup or cereal bowl, and the cover, which fitted inside, had a slight crown. This was redesigned in the 1960s so that the box now has straight sides and the cover laps over an internal lip and is flush with the sides. The diameter of the new design, while cataloged as being the same as the old style, is somewhat smaller.

111/I Wayside Harmony, *TMK-4.*

111 Wayside Harmony

Indicator	Size	Status	TMK-1	TMK-2	TMK-3	TMK-4	TMK-5	TMK-6
111/3/0	4"	P	225	135	85	73	64	58
111.	5½"	D	400	—	—	—	—	—
111/I	5"	P	300	200	150	120	100	90
111	5"	D	350	250	—	—	—	—

The name of this figure has almost as many variations as it has differences in sizes. A 1947 catalog lists this as "Boy on Fence." "Fence Duet," "Duet," and "Boy Just Resting" are other versions in addition to the German *Vaters G'scheitester* for "Father's Cleverest." This has been reported with a yellow shirt in 111/3/0 with TMK-2 and 3. When found add about 50 percent to figures above. In 1980, a reader reported a unique example of this figurine with shiny, white overglaze. Ars Edition has issued graphic H 289 from the drawing they own. Hum. 111 was introduced about 1938, and some examples are incised with that date.

II/111 Wayside Harmony, *Table Lamp, 7½" high. Scarce, same design as Hum. 224, pictured. Dous Collection.*

II/111 Wayside Harmony, Table Lamp

Indicator	Size	Status	TMK-1	TMK-2	TMK-3	TMK-4	TMK-5	TMK-6
II/111	7½"	D	550	450	350	—	—	—

The Roman prefix II designates this as a table lamp created from figure 111. There are only minor differences in sizes. This 7½" lamp was superseded at a later date by 224/I as the 7½" size, and 224/II as the 9½" size. The II/111 lamp is considered scarce. To date it has only been reported with the above marks.

112/I Just Resting, *TMK-5.*

112 Just Resting

Indicator	Size	Status	TMK-1	TMK-2	TMK-3	TMK-4	TMK-5	TMK-6
112/3/0	4"	P	225	130	85	75	65	58
112.	5½"	D	400	300?	—	—	—	—
112	5½"	D	325	200	—	—	—	—
112/I	5"	P	300	200	135	115	100	90

While this is also known as "Girl on Fence" (1947), "Girl Just Resting," and in German, *Mutters Liebste,* for "Mother's Most Beloved," it is obviously a companion piece to Wayside Harmony, Hum. 111, and the pair makes an attractive display. At least one report has been made of an example without the basket at the girl's feet. Such a sample would carry a 100 percent premium if it can be ascertained that it left the factory in that manner. Ars Edition, who owns the original, produced at least one graphic of it as print H 290.

Key to Symbols: A — Assigned; C — Cancelled; D — Discontinued; O — Open; P — Produced; R — Reissued; (?) Examples Doubtful; (—) Examples Unlikely.

II/112 Just Resting, Table Lamp

Indicator	Size	Status	TMK-1	TMK-2	TMK-3	TMK-4	TMK-5	TMK-6
II/112	7½″	D	500	400	300	—	—	—

This 7½″ table lamp was superseded by 225/I and 225/II for the 9½″ size. II/112 carries a 1938 copyright incised on the bottom. It is very rare and is hard to distinguish from 225/I, except for minor details such as the smoother bark on the tree of the early one, and, of course, the information on the base as mentioned. It has been found about 8″ high with the incised model number of 2/112/I. Any example of this lamp would be valued for insurance purposes as shown above.

II/112 **Just Resting,** *Table Lamp, 7½″ high. Rare, same design as Hum. 225, pictured.*

113 Heavenly Song, Candleholder

Indicator	Size	Status	TMK-1	TMK-2	TMK-3	TMK-4	TMK-5	TMK-6
113	3½″	D	5,000	4,000	3,000	—	1,500	105

This candleholder is similar to two others, Hum. 31, Advent Group with Black Child, and Hum. 54, Silent Night. It was reintroduced in limited quantities in Germany in 1978, and was first listed in two U.S. catalogs in 1980. During 1981 Hum. 113 was again discontinued. Whether or not any were made with TMK-6 is not known. It is reported this action was taken because of the confusion caused concerning "lookalikes," Hum. 31 and 54.

113 **Heavenly Song,** *Candleholder. recently discontinued; was always scarce. will become extremely rare. Miller Collection.*

114 Let's Sing, Ashtray

Indicator	Size	Status	TMK-1	TMK-2	TMK-3	TMK-4	TMK-5	TMK-6
114	3½″	D,a	800	700	—	—	—	—
114	3½″	P,b	—	—	100	75	70	63
114.	3½″	D,a	900	800	—	—	—	—

(a – ashtray on viewer's left. b – ashtray on viewer's right.)

This ashtray uses the same design as the figurine, Let's Sing, Hum. 110 (see 110 for more details). Its popularity has jumped since the motif was used on the First Annual Bell, Hum. 700, in 1978. When found with the ashtray on the boy's right (viewer's left) and Crown mark, it is considered rare. The one with current marks has the tray on the boy's left (viewer's right). One interesting example has been found in the new style (ashtray on the boy's left) but with the TMK-2. Hum. 114 has been in the line since the late 1930s.

115, 116, 117 Advent Candlesticks. *(L to R): 117, 115, 116,
TMK-5.*

115 Advent Candlestick, Girl with Nosegay

Indicator	Size	Status	TMK-1	TMK-2	TMK-3	TMK-4	TMK-5	TMK-6
115	3½"	P	100?	70?	40	35	30	25

116 Advent Candlestick, Girl with Fir Tree

Indicator	Size	Status	TMK-1	TMK-2	TMK-3	TMK-4	TMK-5	TMK-6
116	3½"	P	100?	70?	40	35	30	25

117 Advent Candlestick, Boy with Horse

Indicator	Size	Status	TMK-1	TMK-2	TMK-3	TMK-4	TMK-5	TMK-6
117	3½"	P	100?	70?	40	35	30	25

In the 1930s Arthur Möller or Reinhold Unger sculpted three small Advent candleholders similar to Hum. 115, 116, and 117. However, Sister Hummel did not approve the molds for release. Goebel, therefore, took the last three letters of Sister Hummel's name, Mel, and marketed the small candleholders as Mel 1, Mel 2, and Mel 3. These pieces were called "The Christmas Trio," or *Weihnachts-Trio,* in an independently written and published catalog of the early 1950s. Sometime in the early 1960s, Gerhard Skrobek, the present master sculptor at Goebel, redesigned these candleholders and obtained the convent's approval of the figurines. Consequently, the Advent candleholders have been released as Hum. 115, 116, and 117. Any "Mel" examples found would be valued in the mid-hundreds. The Hummel trio is also listed in current catalogs as a set of "Christmas Angels"; the individual names shown above are translations of the German names of these pieces. See *Hummel Art II* for the complete story on Mel figurines.

118 Little Thrifty, Bank

Indicator	Size	Status	TMK-1	TMK-2	TMK-3	TMK-4	TMK-5	TMK-6
118	5"	D,b	370	270	—	—	—	—
118	5½"	D,a	—	—	500	—	—	—
118	5"	P,c	—	—	125	90?	70	63

(a – gold-like coin and thin base. b – silver-colored coin and thick base. c – silver-colored coin and thin base.)

This figurine functions as a bank, and the slot at the top is actually for coins. It has a metal door on the bottom which locks with a key. While this is found with all trademarks, it was not listed in many of the early catalogs, which probably accounts for the scarcity of the model in TMK-1 and 2. The prices above allow for this difference in availability. The early models had a

118 Little Thrifty, *Bank,
model with thin base, TMK-3.*

base that was almost 1″ thick. When it was redesigned, the thickness was reduced to about ¾″, as it is at present. Ars Edition owns the original drawing which shows some German words on the side of the bank. The publishers have produced graphics and cataloged it H 163.

119 Postman

Indicator	Size	Status	TMK-1	TMK-2	TMK-3	TMK-4	TMK-5	TMK-6
119.	5″	D	350	270	—	—	—	—
119	5″	P	300	225	125	100?	87	79

While presently listed in one name and only one size, various old catalogs show the sizes ranging from 4¾″ in 1956 to as much as 5½″ in 1966. The very large or very small sizes would merit a 20 percent premium. Probably designed before 1940 and introduced before the war, it was redesigned in the 1960s with the new, rougher modeled or textured finish, and with the cap tilted to the left rather than straight back as in the older models. The name used for this model in Germany is *Eilbote,* or "Special Messenger." Sister Hummel's original drawing has been reproduced and issued by Ars Edition as graphic H 246.

119 Postman, *TMK-3.*

120 Joyful/Let's Sing, Bookends

Indicator	Size	Status	TMK-1	TMK-2	TMK-3	TMK-4	TMK-5	TMK-6
120	?		—	—	—	—	—	—

The Goebel Company records this as an edition that was closed in the late 1930s and states that there is no known example at the time this book was prepared, not even a factory sample. Any collector who is fortunate to own such a piece, and it is possible, should consider the value in the high four-digit figures. See Joyful, Hum. 53, and Let's Sing, Hum. 110, for more information and related originals and graphics.

121 Wayside Harmony and Just Resting Bookends

Indicator	Size	Status	TMK-1	TMK-2	TMK-3	TMK-4	TMK-5	TMK-6
121	?		—	—	—	—	—	—

This pair was listed as a Closed Edition by the factory in the late 1930s and there is no indication that any were made; there is not even a factory sample known. These, as are Hum. 120 and Hum. 122, are designed by placing the figures directly on the wooden base which carries the number and trademark. They represent another challenge to the well-informed and sharp-eyed collector to be the first to acquire such a set which would be valued in the high four-digit figures. It is likely that they would be glued directly on the wooden base (similar to Doll Mother, 76 A).

122 Puppy Love and Serenade, Bookends

Indicator	Size	Status	TMK-1	TMK-2	TMK-3	TMK-4	TMK-5	TMK-6
122	?		—	—	—	—	—	—

Another pair of Closed Edition bookends using figurines Puppy Love, Hum. 1, and Serenade, Hum. 85; the factory sample indicates that the subjects were mounted directly on the wooden bookend bases and that a dog was used with Serenade to balance the one with Puppy Love. When and if any more are found, they would be rare examples, indeed, as the record indicates these were discontinued in the late 1930s. The value of such a pair would be in the mid four-digit figures or more.

123 Max and Moritz, *TMK-5.*

123 Max and Moritz

Indicator	Size	Status	TMK-1	TMK-2	TMK-3	TMK-4	TMK-5	TMK-6
123	5″	P	280	225	110	95	80	74

These were introduced in the 1940s. Some of the early catalogs do not list them, but the catalogs that do show that the size ranged from the present 5″ high to 5½″ high in 1956. One reader sent a picture of this pair with their heads actually joined (TMK-1 and 2 marks), indicating the possible variables that can occur when the component parts are assembled by the "garnisher" at the factory. The early figurines carry a 1939 copyright date, even with the TMK-3, which were restyled in about the 1960s. The prices given allow for any minor style and color changes. The German name, *Max und Moritz,* is similar to the English. Ars Edition issues graphics of this pair from Sister Hummel's original drawing which they own. The catalog number is H 352.

124 Hello, *TMK-5.*

124 Hello

Indicator	Size	Status	TMK-1	TMK-2	TMK-3	TMK-4	TMK-5	TMK-6
124/0	6¼″	D	—	224	150	—	—	—
124.	6¼″	D	350	—	—	—	—	—
124/0	6¼″	P	—	—	110	95	85	74
124/I	6¾″	D	700	500	350	—	—	—
124/I	6¾″	D,a	—	—	—	—	115	105

(a – temporarily discontinued in 1982.)

On page 173 of *Hummel Art II,* is a picture of six different versions of Hum. 124 figurines, called *Der Chef* in German ("The Boss" in English), with various colored cutaways and striped trousers. Generally speaking, the older marks, especially TMK-1, were produced with a gray-green coat and pants, while TMK-2 and TMK-3 wore different shades of brown coats and pants. When they were restyled and reissued they reverted to a brown and gray combination. It is probably best to rely on the price table above, keeping in mind the generalities about colors. The original drawing has been reproduced as graphic H 239 by Ars Edition.

125 Vacation Time, Plaque

Indicator	Size	Status	TMK-1	TMK-2	TMK-3	TMK-4	TMK-5	TMK-6
125	5"	D,a	500	400	—	—	—	—
125	4¾"	P,b	—	—	150	125	105	95

(a – fence has six upright posts. b – fence has five upright posts.)

Even though this plaque is not found in many of the catalogs from the 1950s, it is found with all trademarks. One way of distinguishing the early plaques from those of the later 1960s is by counting the number of posts in the fence. Originally, there were six posts; later plaques have only five posts. In her original drawing, Sister Hummel had five posts in front of the children. This drawing has been transferred photomechanically into Ars Edition grapic H 206. In earlier catalogs this was called "On Holiday," and the German *Ferienfreude, Bild,* reads "Vacation Friends, Picture."

125 Vacation Time, *Plaque, known with six fence uprights (scarce), TMK-5.*

126 Retreat to Safety, Plaque

Indicator	Size	Status	TMK-1	TMK-2	TMK-3	TMK-4	TMK-5	TMK-6
126	4¾"	P	325	200	140	125	105	95

Issued before World War II, this plaque is not found in many early U.S. catalogs, as is the case with a number of plaques and other auxiliary articles. Some size variations of minor importance have been recorded. The English name has remained unchanged, although the German name *Bild, Angsthase* has the stronger derogatory connotation, which is "Coward." This is the same motif as the figurine of the same name, Hum. 201. (See 201 for further details.) There is also some similarity between this very rare bas-relief plaque and the even rarer figurine, Little Velma, 219/2/0, which depicts a girl seated on the fence rather than a boy. This plaque was added to one U.S. catalog in 1978.

126 Retreat to Safety, *Plaque. TMK-5.*

127 Doctor

Indicator	Size	Status	TMK-1	TMK-2	TMK-3	TMK-4	TMK-5	TMK-6
127	4¾"	P	275	140	100	75?	67	60

Since being introduced before 1947, there have been various sizes produced that have ranged from about 4¾" high to slightly over 5" high. One catalog may have been in error in listing it at 3½", as no examples have been reported this small. This piece has been reproduced extensively by several companies with striking fidelity. Be sure any piece acquired has the M.I. Hummel facsimile signature. The German name, *Puppendoctor,* or "Doll Doctor" is a somewhat more realistic name. The original drawing, owned by Ars Edition, has been reproduced and cataloged as H 256. A picture of the figurine is shown for the January 1960 and also the October 1972 calendar pages.

127 Doctor, *TMK-5.*

128 Baker, *TMK-5*.

128 Baker

Indicator	Size	Status	TMK-1	TMK-2	TMK-3	TMK-4	TMK-5	TMK-6
128	4¾"	P	275	250	110	90?	75	69

This figurine has been in the line since before 1946 without any record of important changes except for the restyling that many figurines underwent in the 1960s when Skrobek introduced a rougher textured finish and a brighter palette of colors. Over the years the size has varied from about 4½" high to 5" high compared to the present standard of 4¾". The German name is *Der Kleinge Konditor*, which means "Little Confectioner." Sister Hummel's original drawing is now owned by Ars Edition and published as print H 243. The figurine itself is pictured for the month of April in the 1975 calendar.

129 Band Leader, *TMK-3*.

129 Band Leader

Indicator	Size	Status	TMK-1	TMK-2	TMK-3	TMK-4	TMK-5	TMK-6
129	5"	P	300	150	125	100?	90	84

This model was in production before 1946. The sizes in the catalogs of that time range up to 5½" high, compared to the present standard of 5" high. Examples of this intense leader have been reported with the music printed upside-down. Such would certainly be a premium piece (perhaps 50 percent over listed prices). This figurine has the same name as the German one, *Herr Kapellmeister*. The original drawing is owned by Ars Edition who issued it as print H 248. The figurine is pictured on the January 1972 calendar page.

130 Duet, *TMK-5*.

130 Duet

Indicator	Size	Status	TMK-1	TMK-2	TMK-3	TMK-4	TMK-5	TMK-6
130	5"	D,a	450	—	—	—	—	—
130	5"	P,b	350	225	150	125?	110	100

(a — base with overhang. b — straight-side base.)

In the 1947 catalog the price was $6. The name is a contraction of the German *Duett, Sangerpaar*, "Singing Pair." This pair appears to be the inspiration for both the Street Singer, Hum. 131, and the Soloist, Hum. 135. The original Sister Hummel drawing from which this motif was adapted actually portrays a nocturnal quartet. The nearest two figures were selected for use as this figurine. The original scene has been accurately shown in H 577, published by Ars Edition, owner of the original drawing.

131 Street Singer

Indicator	Size	Status	TMK-1	TMK-2	TMK-3	TMK-4	TMK-5	TMK-6
131	5″	P	250	120	90	80?	70	63

This model was once called "Singer," Hum. 131. A later catalog from the early 1950s carries the name "Soloist," which is now assigned to Hum. 135, which, at that time, was known as "High Tenor." The original German name, *Kammersänger*, would translate as "Chamber Singer." This figurine has been found in all trademarks with some color differences not sufficient enough to affect the prices. It is pictured for the month of January in the 1973 calendar and appears as second singer from the right in Ars Edition print H 577.

131 Street Singer, *TMK-5.*

132 Star Gazer

Indicator	Size	Status	TMK-1	TMK-2	TMK-3	TMK-4	TMK-5	TMK-6
132	4¾″	D,a	300	200	150	—	—	—
132	4¾″	P,b	—	—	125	115?	93	84
132	5″	D,c	400	—	—	—	—	—

(a – blue shirt. b – purple shirt. c – blue shirt, black scope.)

Since at least 1947, this model has been called "Star Gazer" in both English and German *(Sterngucker)*. The color of the shirt appears to have been more of a true blue than the reddish blue now used. One TMK-5 has been reported in white overglaze which makes one wonder whether some of these odd white pieces were possibly "lunchbox" samples. A picture of Hum. 132 is shown for November in the 1978 calendar. Sister Hummel's original work has been lithographed as print H 242 by Ars Edition, who owns the original drawing.

132 Star Gazer, *TMK-5.*

133 Mother's Helper

Indicator	Size	Status	TMK-1	TMK-2	TMK-3	TMK-4	TMK-5	TMK-6
133	5″	P	325	175	125	105?	94	84

This model is a favorite for feline fanciers because it is presently the only M.I. Hummel with a cat. This has not been consistently listed in all catalogs over the years, even though it is found with all trademarks. A similar figurine that may be released in the future was copyrighted on July 18, 1956, as "Mother's Good Helper" and assigned the number Hum. 325. This appears to be almost identical to Sister Hummel's original drawing, which included a table with the cat positioned differently. Graphics include a large size print H 201, by Ars Edition, who owns the original drawing.

133 Mother's Helper, *TMK-3.*

134 Quartet, Plaque

Indicator	Size	Status	TMK-1	TMK-2	TMK-3	TMK-4	TMK-5	TMK-6
134	6″	P	475	270	190	165?	155	140

The group in this bas-relief plaque was adapted from an original by Sister Hummel that shows these four boys standing in a row entertaining on a street corner. It was published as a graphic by Ars Edition from the original drawing in their possession and cataloged H 284. While only slight variations are found in the front, the back was redesigned so that the present plaques have a centered hole for wall mounting on a nail or patented hanger. Older marks are found with two holes for picture wire or cord. This piece has been called by the same name over the years, with the German name of *Das Quartett, Bild,* and includes the two figures on the left in Sister Hummel's original who were omitted from Duet, Hum. 130. The older pieces have M. J. Hummel incised on the back; the new ones are incised on the front.

134 Quartet, *Plaque, TMK-5.*

135 Soloist

Indicator	Size	Status	TMK-1	TMK-2	TMK-3	TMK-4	TMK-5	TMK-6
135	4¾″	P	220	110	80	70?	60	53

When the companion piece, Street Singer, Hum. 131, was called "Soloist" in the early 1950s, Hum. 135 was called "High Tenor," which comes closer to the English translation of "Heroic Tenor" for the German word *Heldentenor.* Known in all trademarks and currently specified as 4¾″ high, older catalogs indicate that the height has ranged from 4¼″ to 5¼″ over the last thirty years. Any example over 5″ would warrant a premium of 10 to 20 percent. A full color picture of this figurine is in the 1972 calendar for the month of January. It is also the second figure from the right in Sister Hummel's original drawing and in Ars Edition graphic H 284, which was made from the original.

135 Soloist, *TMK-5.*

136 Friends

Indicator	Size	Status	TMK-1	TMK-2	TMK-3	TMK-4	TMK-5	TMK-6
136	11″	D,a	5,000+	—	—	—	—	—
136	10½″	D,b	6,000+	—	—	—	—	—
136.	10½″	D,c	2,000	—	—	—	—	—
136/I	5″	P,d	350?	200	130	100?	95	84
136/V	10½″	P,d	1,500	900	700	600?	550	500
136/V(5)	10½″	D,c	1,700	1,000	800	—	—	—

(a – white overglaze finish. b – terra-cotta finish. c – three rows of dots. d – two rows of dots.)

The copyright date on the back of the smaller sizes is 1947. The smaller size, 136/I, had varied from at least 4¼″ to 5¼″ by 1966. The 10½″ size was listed as 136 (only) in the early 1950s; the 10½″ size is also known with 136. (decimal). A very rare version of Hum. 136 made of brick red terra-cotta and white glaze is known.

136/I Friends, *copyright 1947, TMK-5.*

137 A&B Child in Bed, Plaque

Indicator	Size	Status	TMK-1	TMK-2	TMK-3	TMK-4	TMK-5	TMK-6
137	2¾"	R	—	—	—	—	35	30
137/B	2¾"	D	300	150	100	45?	40	—

137 **Child in Bed**, *Plaque*, *TMK-5*.

This plaque was first issued in two versions differentiated by the markings 137 A and 137 B incised on the backs. When marked 137 A, the child was looking to the viewer's right. The other one of the pair, 137 B, showed the child looking at the ladybug and to the viewer's left. A 1959 U.S. catalog lists only the one version marked 137 (only), 3" in diameter. Apparently, 137 (only) superseded the former 137 B with the child looking at the ladybug. The other model, 137 A, must have been discontinued very early, as there have been no examples reported to date. Ba-Bee Rings have bees; Child in Bed has a ladybug. The German name, *Bild, Kind im Bett,* means "Child in Small Bed."

138 Tiny Baby in Crib, Plaque

Indicator	Size	Status	TMK-1	TMK-2	TMK-3	TMK-4	TMK-5	TMK-6
138	3"	C	?	2,000+	—	—	—	—

In *Hummel Art I,* Hum. 138 was listed as "Unknown," and by the factory as CN for "Closed Number" never to be used again. Further search of the factory records resulted in locating a sample which shows an infant as titled. Since then a reader in Illinois has reported an example of this rarity which he purchased in Germany in 1951. This exciting discovery should be valued in the low four-digit figures, as the factory is of the opinion that this was never offered for sale.

138 **Tiny Baby in Crib**, *Plaque.*
TMK-2. Miller Collection.

139 Flitting Butterfly, Plaque

Indicator	Size	Status	TMK-1	TMK-2	TMK-3	TMK-4	TMK-5	TMK-6
139	2½"	D,a	350	—	—	—	—	—
139	2½"	R,b	250	160	80	—	40	30

(a – red dress, no dots. b – orange dress with dots.)

The early marks show a smaller baby with a darker red dress with no dots and an open space behind the baby's neck. The new, larger model, apparently redesigned in the 1960s, was introduced in the U.S. for the first time in all catalogs in 1980. Prior to 1980, examples of the redesigned model with TMK-5 were available only from German dealers. This piece continues to command a premium because of the scarcity.

139 **Flitting Butterfly**, *Plaque. (Left) reinstated, current design. (Right) old design, no dots on dress. Miller Collection.*

140 The Mail Is Here, Plaque

Indicator	Size	Status	TMK-1	TMK-2	TMK-3	TMK-4	TMK-5	TMK-6
140	4½″	P,a	375	275	175	150	130	120
140	4½″	D,b	2,000	—	—	—	—	—

(*a – regular color plaque.* *b – white overglaze plaque.*)

In the Alphabetical Index, this plaque has been listed as above, but it is also known as "Mail Coach" by many collectors. This plaque has been reported to have been made in a plain white overglaze with TMK-2. About 1952, this design was released as a three-dimensional figurine, Hum. 226 (see 226 for more information).

140 The Mail Is Here, *Plaque,* *TMK-5.*

141 Apple Tree Girl

Indicator	Size	Status	TMK-1	TMK-2	TMK-3	TMK-4	TMK-5	TMK-6
141/3/0	4″	D,a	250	200	—	—	—	—
141/3/0	4″	P,b	—	95	70	65	69	53
141.	6″	D,a	500	400	300	—	—	—
141	6″	D,a	400	300	200	—	—	—
141/I	6″	P,a	300	175	150	125	110	100
141/V	10″	P,b	—	—	—	625	550	500
141/X	32″	P,b	—	—	—	—	13,000	12,500

(*a – tapered base as tree trunk.* *b – regular white vertical base.*)

The present English name and "Spring," a foreshortening of the German name, *Frühling, Mädchen im Baum,* were used in various early catalogs. First issued in the 6″ to 6½″ size and marked 141 (only) or 141. (decimal). Both 141/I and 141/3/0 have been found in TMK-1. In both of the early sizes, the base and tree trunk appeared as one. The smaller 141/3/0 size is the only one issued without a bird in the top of the tree. The next recorded size, 141/V, was introduced around 1970. The giant size, 141/X, which varies around 32″ high, was first available in the U.S. in 1976. One marked 141 (only) in white overglaze would be valued in the very low four-digit figures.

141/I Apple Tree Girl, *TMK-5.*

142 Apple Tree Boy

Indicator	Size	Status	TMK-1	TMK-2	TMK-3	TMK-4	TMK-5	TMK-6
142/3/0	4″	D,a	250	200	—	—	—	—
142/3/0	4″	P,b	—	95	70	65	60	53
142.	6″	D,a	500	400	300	—	—	—
142	6″	D,a	400	300	200	—	—	—
142/I	6″	P,b	300	175	150	125	110	100
142/V	10″	P,b	—	—	—	625	550	500
142/X	32″	P,b	—	—	—	—	13,000	12,000

(*a – tapered base as tree trunk.* *b – regular white vertical base.*)

This one was also known as "Fall," as the German name, *Herbst, Junge im Baum,* implies. Ars Edition produces graphics of this pair from their originals as H 297 and H 298. The motifs are also used for the 1975 and 1976 Annual Plates, Hum. 269 and 270; Lamps, Hum. 229 and 230; and Bookends, Hum. 252 A and B. Hum. 142 (only) in white overglaze would be valued in the very low four-digit figures.

142/I Apple Tree Boy, *TMK-1.*

143 Boots

Indicator	Size	Status	TMK-1	TMK-2	TMK-3	TMK-4	TMK-5	TMK-6
143/0	5½″	P	275	150	95	85	75	69
143.	6¾″	D	350	450	—	—	—	—
143/I	6½″	R	375	225	175	135	115	105
143/I	6½″	D,a	500	—	—	—	—	—

(a – unusual example with black apron.)

Sometime in the early 1950s the 143 (only) was superseded by 143/I for figures in this height. This size has not been continuously available in the U.S. and was reintroduced in Germany in limited quantities in 1978; it is now available from U.S. distributors. The smaller size, Hum. 143/3/0, was listed in some of the early 1950s catalogs and called "Shoemaker," and varied from 4½″ high to the present 5½″ high. The German name has no relation to the English one as it translates as "Mister Important" from *Meister Wichtig*. Ars Edition has published an exact likeness of the original work in graphics as H 255.

143/0 Boots, *TMK-5.*

144 Angelic Song

Indicator	Size	Status	TMK-1	TMK-2	TMK-3	TMK-4	TMK-5	TMK-6
144	4″	P	250	125	100	75	68	60

Introduced before 1947, a catalog of that year lists the name as "Singing Angel," 4¼″ high, for $5. A much more descriptive name, "Angel with Mandolin, Girl with Hymn Book," was used in the early 1950s. The German name is *Singendes Kind mit Engelein,* meaning "Singing Child with Small Angel." Aside from the small differences in height, other reported variations include some slight deviation in the blue flowers in the headband. The nearest graphic that has been found is Ars Edition H 386.

144 Angelic Song, *TMK-5.*

145 Little Guardian

Indicator	Size	Status	TMK-1	TMK-2	TMK-3	TMK-4	TMK-5	TMK-6
145	4″	D,a	375	150	110	—	—	—
145	4″	P,b	300	130	90	75	65	60

(a – headband has blue flowers. b – headband has orange flowers.)

The catalog history of this pair shows the height varying widely from as small as 3¾″ in 1950 to as tall as 4¾″ in 1959. Since the table above reflects the current size of 4″, examples 4½″ and larger should be valued at a premium of about 20 percent. The headband on the kneeling child is also found with blue flowers instead of the present orange ones. The German name for this pair is *Betendes Kind mit Engelein,* which means "Praying Child with Small Angel." "Angel Pair" and "Girl Kneeling Beside Angel with Flowers" are other names used over the last thirty-five years. No original drawing by Sister Hummel with this motif has been located to date.

145 Little Guardian, *TMK-3.*

146 Angel Duet, *Holy Water Font,*
TMK-4.

146 Angel Duet, Holy Water Font

Indicator	Size	Status	TMK-1	TMK-2	TMK-3	TMK-4	TMK-5	TMK-6
146	4¾"	P	90	45	35	30	25	22

Some of the older catalogs of the 1950s refer to this piece as Holy Water Font, Hum. 146, slightly larger than the above listed size. The present name, Angel Duet, is confusing because it is also used for two other models which are not the same figures. One is a candleholder, Hum. 193, and another is a very similar figurine of two angels singing from a common hymn book, Hum 261. Hum. 146 is found in all trademarks and the later models have a palette of colors brighter than the earlier ones. The location of Sister Hummel's original drawing for this motif has not been verified as yet.

147 Angel Shrine, Holy Water Font

Indicator	Size	Status	TMK-1	TMK-2	TMK-3	TMK-4	TMK-5	TMK-6
147	5"	P	90	50	35	30	25	22

In *Hummel Art I,* this font was listed with the primary name "Devotion" and the secondary name "Angel Shrine." These have now been reversed, as only one catalog now lists this font as "Devotion." Some of the early catalogs referred to this as "Angel at Shrine." Although not listed in many catalogs, it was introduced by 1950, and it is found with all trademarks. The height listed varies from about 5" to 5½" high. Note how the tips of the wings join the shrine roof to reduce the hazard of damage to the fragile wings. The font has been found in TMK-2 with one extra flower to the left of the angel. The original drawing is owned by Ars Edition, who has faithfully duplicated it as graphic H 444.

147 Angel Shrine, *Holy Water Font,*
TMK-3. (Alternate name, Devotion.)
Dous Collection.

148 Cancelled Number

Indicator	Size	Status	TMK-1	TMK-2	TMK-3	TMK-4	TMK-5	TMK-6
148	?	U	—	—	—	—	—	—

According to *HUMMEL, Authorized Supplement* by Robert L. Miller, the factory records indicate that this number was not used after 1941 and may have been intended for some version of Farm Boy. While it is unlikely that a sample will ever be discovered in or out of the factory, there is always the slight chance that some diligent collector or researcher will find one which would be valued in the high four-digit figures.

149 Cancelled Number

Indicator	Size	Status	TMK-1	TMK-2	TMK-3	TMK-4	TMK-5	TMK-6
149	?	U	—	—	—	—	—	—

Factory records indicate that this number was not used after 1941 and may have been intended for a variation of the Goose Girl, according to Robert L. Miller. While it is unlikely that any sample is extant, sometime, someplace, one may be ferreted out by a dedicated collector who will then have a prized possession valued at $5,000 or more.

150 Happy Days

Indicator	Size	Status	TMK-1	TMK-2	TMK-3	TMK-4	TMK-5	TMK-6
150/2/0	4¼″	P	—	150	120	100	90	79
150/0	5¼″	R	500	250	180	—	130	120
150	6¼″	D	550	—	—	—	—	—
150.	6¼″	D	600	400	—	—	—	—
150/I	6¼″	R	650	450	?	—	250	230

The earliest listing found was in 1947. In the early 1950s, it was also incised with only the model number 150 at 15.5 cm, or slightly over 6″ high. By 1959, the 5″ size, 150/0, and the 4″ size, 150/2/0, were shown, but with no mention of the larger size. In 1966, only the smallest size 150/2/0 was listed as 4¼″ tall. The other two sizes marked 150/0 at 5¼″ and 150/I at 6¼″ (which superseded 150 only) were reintroduced in 1979 in very limited quantities. Ars Edition has produced graphic H 338 and owns the original drawing.

150/2/0 Happy Days, *TMK-5.*

151 Madonna Holding Child

Indicator	Size	Status	TMK-1	TMK-2	TMK-3	TMK-4	TMK-5	TMK-6
151	12″	R,a	4,000	3,000	—	—	500	450
151	12″	R,b	3,000	2,000	—	—	180	165
151	12″	D,c	5,000	—	—	—	—	—
151	12″	D,d	9,000	—	—	—	—	—
151	12″	D,e	8,000	—	—	—	—	—

(a – light blue cloak. b – white overglaze cloak. c – dark blue cloak. d – dark brown cloak. e – ivory cloak.)

This figurine was known in the mid-1970s as·the very rare "Blue Cloak Madonna." Later, an example in white surfaced and, in 1977, a brown one was added to the well-known Robert and Ruth Miller collection. These were selling in the mid four-digit range until Goebel decided to reintroduce both the blue and the white version in 1978 in Germany at a small fraction of the price. The present price for a Hum. 151, with TMK-5 or 6, is about one-tenth the price of an old one, but still expensive compared to a similarly sized Flower Madonna, Hum. 19. At present, other rare versions of this Madonna are known in a dark blue cloak and in an ivory colored cloak. These two and the one in brown have not been reissued to date, but the possibility always exists. Collectors should be especially well informed when acquiring an old example of this model number as to what premium they are paying for an old mark on the bottom. There is always the chance of paying too high a price for even one with late TMK-5 or 6. Goebel's future production plans are the key factor. The German name, *Sitzende Madonna mit sitzendem Kind,* translates as "Sitting Madonna with Seated Child." Numerous madonnas are known to have been drawn by Sister Hummel, but none exactly matches this one.

151 Madonna Holding Child *(with blue cloak), TMK-5, courtesy W. Goebel Co.*

151 Madonna Holding Child *(with brown cloak), TMK-5, courtesy W. Goebel Co.*

152A Umbrella Boy

Indicator	Size	Status	TMK-1	TMK-2	TMK-3	TMK-4	TMK-5	TMK-6
152/0/A	4¾″	D,a	—	800	—	—	—	—
152/0/A	4¾″	P,b	—	600	450	325	275	250
152.	8″	D	1,500	—	—	—	—	—
152A	8″	D	1,200	1,000	900	—	—	—
152/A/II	8″	P	—	900	875	825	780	720

(a – copyright date incised 1951. b – copyright date incised 1957.)

152/A/0 Umbrella Boy, *TMK-4.*

The model was first produced sometime in the 1940s and listed in a 1950 catalog as "Boy Under Roof," at 7¾″ high, incised only 152. In a 1956 catalog, this was then called "In Safety" and incised as 152A only, about 8″ high. The companion 152B, Umbrella Girl, was also listed in this catalog. By 1959, the smaller 4¾″ size had been introduced as an addition to the large 8″ size. At that time, they were designated 152/O/A and 152/A/II, respectively. The U.S. Copyright Office shows the registration date as January 17, 1951, with revisions in 1957 and again in 1972.

152B Umbrella Girl

Indicator	Size	Status	TMK-1	TMK-2	TMK-3	TMK-4	TMK-5	TMK-6
152/0/B	4¾″	D,a	—	800	—	—	—	—
152/0/B	4¾″	P,b	—	600	450	325	275	250
152B	8″	D	1,200	1,000	900	—	—	—
152/B/II	8″	P	—	900	875	825	780	720

(a – copyright date incised 1951. b – copyright date incised 1957.)

152/B/0 Umbrella Girl, *TMK-4.*

Since some of the early catalogs list only the number 152 for "Boy Under Roof," it appears that this companion piece was introduced somewhat later, but before 1956. Otherwise, the remarks above about 152A apply as well to Umbrella Girl. Both 152 A and B have been produced in graphics by Ars Edition as H 294 and H 296.

153 Auf Wiedersehen

Indicator	Size	Status	TMK-1	TMK-2	TMK-3	TMK-4	TMK-5	TMK-6
153/0	5″	D,a	—	1,800	—	—	—	—
153/0	5″	P	—	170	130	110	100	90
153.	7″	D	700	—	—	—	—	—
153/I	7″	R	480	240	180	—	130	120
153	7″	D	600	—	—	—	—	—

(a – some with TMK-2 have boy with hat, rare.)

153 Auf Wiedersehen, *TMK-5.*

First introduced in the 1940s, it was called "Goodbye," incised with only the model number 153, and measured about 7″ high. Sometime in the early 1950s the name was changed in the English catalogs to the well-known German *Auf Wiedersehen.* Some of these early small 153/0, TMK-2, were made with the boy wearing a hat and not waving a handkerchief. The large 7″ size was apparently uncataloged for years until it was reintroduced in limited quantities in 1977 in the U.S. The original drawing owned by Ars Edition and issued as graphic H 210 was modified considerably for the figurine.

154 Waiter

Indicator	Size	Status	TMK-1	TMK-2	TMK-3	TMK-4	TMK-5	TMK-6
154/0	6″	P,b	300	175	122	105	93	84
154	6½″	D,a	600	—	—	—	—	—
154.	6½″	D,a	700	—	—	—	—	—
154/I	7″	P,b	400	200	140	—	116	105

(a – old example, gray coat and trousers. b – new example, blue coat and tan trousers.)

154/0 **Waiter**, *with brown pants, trademark unknown.*

In the 1950s this was called "Little Waiter," and incised with only the 154. When the smaller size, which is now 6″ high, was introduced, it was marked 154/0; about the same time the large one, now 7″ high, was introduced as 154/I. During the early period the Waiter had a gray jacket and striped gray pants. This was changed to a blue-gray jacket and tan striped pants. The label on the bottle of the current model carries the name "Rhein Wine," as have most examples in the past. The number of label variations are unknown, but there are several, including an illegible scrawl. Such variations in name would be valued at least 50 percent higher than a standard "Rhein Wine" with similar trademark. It has been reproduced by Ars Edition, who owns the original drawing, as H 244.

155-162 Cancelled Numbers

Indicator	Size	Status	TMK-1	TMK-2	TMK-3	TMK-4	TMK-5	TMK-6
155-162	?		—	—	—	—	—	—

During a five-month period from May through October of 1943, these eight numbers were cancelled by the Goebel Company for unknown reasons. According to Robert L. Miller's HUMMEL, *Authorized Supplement,* design studies were tentatively assigned to each number. Factory samples show them in more contemporary dress. In the surprising event that one of these designs should surface, it would no doubt be valued in the four-digit range.

163 Whitsuntide

Indicator	Size	Status	TMK-1	TMK-2	TMK-3	TMK-4	TMK-5	TMK-6
163	7″	D,a	900	—	—	—	—	—
163	7″	D,b	800	700	600	—	—	—
163	6½″	P,a	—	—	—	—	130	120

(a – no provision for candle. b – sold with yellow-colored candle)

The German name, *Glockenturm mit Engeln,* which translates as "Bell Tower with Angels," is certainly more descriptive and accurate. So far it appears in all marks except TMK-4. It was reintroduced in very limited quantities in Germany in 1978 and appeared since then in U.S. catalogs. This reintroduction has lowered the price some collectors paid for older marks. The new version is easily distinguished, as it is only 6½″ high as compared to the older one that is about 7″ high. The angel on the base in the latest figurine is not holding a candle as some of the older ones did, but some examples with the Crown mark showed no evidence of a candle, either.

163 **Whitsuntide**, *old design, TMK-2.*

164 Worship, Holy Water Font

Indicator	Size	Status	TMK-1	TMK-2	TMK-3	TMK-4	TMK-5	TMK-6
164	4¾"	D,a	260	120	—	—	—	—
164	4¾"	P,b	—	—	40	35	28	25

(a – old design with stippled edge and no extension in back. b – later design, shaded edge and wider back than bowl.)

At one time this model was called "Praying Girl Font." The older Crown and Full Bee styles are distinguished by a stippled coloring around the edge, compared to the shaded airbrush coloring on later models. The redesigned models also have an extension of the back beyond the semicircular bowl. This was probably introduced in the late 1940s or very early 1950s. The German name, *Am Wegesrand,* translates as "At the Wayside."

164 **Worship,** *Holy Water Font,* *TMK-5. Dous Collection.*

165 Swaying Lullaby, Plaque

Indicator	Size	Status	TMK-1	TMK-2	TMK-3	TMK-4	TMK-5	TMK-6
165	5¼"	D,a	400	300	200	—	85	75
165	5¼"	R,b	—	—	—	—	85	75

(a – incised M.I. Hummel on back. b – incised M. I. Hummel on front.)

For some years this was a very high-priced collectible when found with a Crown or Full Bee trademark. They could be obtained only in the secondary market. In 1978, Goebel reinstated production of this model in very limited quantities in Germany. It is now available through regular channels in the U.S., and the prices for old marks may drop considerably depending on the quantities being produced. The German name *Kind mit Hängematte und Vogel* translate as "Child with Hammock and Bird." The inscription on the front means "Dreaming of Better Times." Reproduction H 120 from the original drawing is published by Ars Edition.

165 **Swaying Lullaby,** *Plaque,* *TMK-2, no copyright date. Miller Collection.*

166 Boy with Bird, Ashtray

Indicator	Size	Status	TMK-1	TMK-2	TMK-3	TMK-4	TMK-5	TMK-6
166	6¼"	P	225	160	105	95	83	75

While this has been found in all trademarks, it was not always cataloged, possibly due to low demand. The boy lying prone differs from Singing Lesson Ashtray, Hum. 34, in which the boy is seated as in the figurine, Hum. 63; the Candy Box, Hum. III/63; and the 1979 Annual Plate, Hum. 272. The bird also varies in design and color. The German name, *Junge mit Vogel,* means "Boy with Bird." The original drawing is owned by Ars Edition who has published a reproduction of the drawing as graphic H 616.

166 **Boy with Bird,** *Ashtray,* *TMK-5.*

167 Angel with Yellow Bird, Holy Water Font

Indicator	Size	Status	TMK-1	TMK-2	TMK-3	TMK-4	TMK-5	TMK-6
167	4¾"	P	150	80	40	30	24	22

This name has been modified since the font, Angel with Birds, Hum. 22, also has seated angel with birds. In this case, the angel is facing to the left with no halo. In Hum. 22, the angel is facing to the right and has a halo. The early TMK-1 and TMK-2 models of Hum. 167 do not have the hanging hole in th top of the font, and the edge of the bowl is stippled with no extension or protruding flange at the back. At that time the width was only about 2″. As with other fonts, this has not been continuously cataloged although it has been produced wih all trademarks.

167 Angel with Yellow Bird, *Holy Water Font, TMK-5.*

168 Standing Boy, Plaque

Indicator	Size	Status	TMK-1	TMK-2	TMK-3	TMK-4	TMK-5	TMK-6
168	5¾"	D,a	450	350	250	---	85	75
168	5¾"	R,b	—	—	—	—	85	75

(a – incised signature on back. b – incised signature on front.)

Another plaque that was a very rare and high-priced collectors' item until 1978 when it was reintroduced in very limited quantities with TMK-5 continues in current production. The price of the old ones has already dropped and future prices will depend on how many of the recent production items are made. The German name, *Stehender Junge mit Herz and Flashe* means "Standing Boy with Heart and Bottle." This plaque and Hum. 399, Valentine Joy, which was the Goebel Collectors' Club limited edition for the 1980-1981 members, were adapted from the same Sister Hummel original which is owned by Ars Edition. An exact replica of this drawing has been published as H 335.

168 Standing Boy, *Plaque, original TMK-2 pictured. Miller Collection.*

169 Bird Duet

Indicator	Size	Status	TMK-1	TMK-2	TMK-3	TMK-4	TMK-5	TMK-6
169	4"	D,a	250	150	110	—	—	—
169	4"	P,b	—	—	90	80	70	63

(a – black baton in raised position. b – brownish red baton in horizontal position.)

Since introduced around 1950, the birds have changed their tune at least three, possibly more times based on the music that appears on the stand. This is only one of innumerable modifications in design, color, and height, some of which were due to general restyling in about 1961. With the TMK-1, 2, and 3 marks (early 1950s) the black baton was raised, as compared to the red baton at rest in the current versions. In the German catalog, spelling was once *Duett*. The present German name deviates from this theme by calling it *Frühlingslied,* for "Song of Spring."

169 Bird Duet, *TMK-5.*

170/I School Boys, *TMK-5.*

170   School Boys

Indicator	Size	Status	TMK-1	TMK-2	TMK-3	TMK-4	TMK-5	TMK-6
170	10″	D	2,000	1,800	—	—	—	—
170/I	7½″	P	—	—	700	625	550	500
170/III	10¼″	D,a	—	—	1,450	1,400	1,300	1,250

(a – in the Spring of 1982, Goebel announced that Hum. 170/III has been discontinued.)

This group was issued around 1950 in just the large 10″ size and incised only 170 on the base. Some of the U.S. catalogs of the mid-1950s do not list this model at all. A smaller size, 7½″, was copyrighted in the U.S. on December 20, 1961, and incised 170/I. The larger 10″ size changed from only 170 to 170/III at about 9½″ to 10¼″ high. The recent restyled pieces are incised 1972; the smaller ones are marked 1961. The German name is *Schwieriges Problem* or "Difficult Problem." Ars Edition, who owns the original drawing, publish a reproduction of it, H 198. See School Girls, Hum. 177, for a companion piece.

171   Little Sweeper

Indicator	Size	Status	TMK-1	TMK-2	TMK-3	TMK-4	TMK-5	TMK-6
171	4¼″	P	200	110	80	70	60	53

Apparently, this was first called "Sweeper" after the German name, *Kehrliesl*, and then changed in the early 1950s to "Girl with Broom" to distinguish it from Mother's Helper, Hum. 133. Finally, before the end of the 1950s, the figurine assumed its present name. The general restyling in the 1960s resulted in brighter colors, a shinier finish, and a more "modern" look. The original drawing is owned by Ars Edition who has published reproduction H 234 from it.

171 Little Sweeper, *TMK-5.*

172   Festival Harmony w/ Mandolin

Indicator	Size	Status	TMK-1	TMK-2	TMK-3	TMK-4	TMK-5	TMK-6
172/0	8″	P,c	—	—	—	150	120	100
172	10½″	D,a	1,500	—	—	—	—	—
172.	10½″	D,a	1,600	—	—	—	—	—
172/II	10½″	D,b	—	500	350	275	—	—
172/II	10½″	P,c	—	—	—	—	250	210

(a – flowers to waist (see illustration). b – flower blossom in front of dress. c – flower on base (see illustration).

First issued about 10″ high with a Crown mark and incised 172, as illustrated, it had the waist-high flower and bird arrangement in front of the angel. This was not listed in many of the early catalogs. It was redesigned showing only a plant with blossoms slightly above the hem. This version is found with the Full Bee mark. In the 1960s, a smaller size, about 8″ high in the new style, was introduced and incised 172/0, and is found usually in TMK-4, 5, and 6. The German name is *Adventsengel mit Mandoline,* "Advent Angel with Mandolin." Ars Edition owns the original drawing and currently reproduces it as H 449.

172 (L) *Old version, TMK-1.*
172/II (R) *New version, TMK-5.*

173 Festival Harmony w/ Flute

Indicator	Size	Status	TMK-1	TMK-2	TMK-3	TMK-4	TMK-5	TMK-6
173/0	8"	P,c	—	—	—	150	120	110
173(.)	10½"	D,a	1,500	—	—	—	—	—
173/II	10½"	D,b	—	500	350	275	—	—
173/II	10½"	P,c	—	—	—	—	250	210

(a – flowers to waist. b – flower blossom in front of dress. c – flower on base.)

Hum. 173 also followed the same progressive changes in design, apparently at exactly the same time, through the 1950s and 1960s. The unavailability at certain periods, the introduction of the smaller size, and the change in model numbering followed in parallel. Presently, the flowers are below the hemline of the angel's gown. Some collectors feel that this version is rarer than the Festival Harmony with Banjo, Hum. 172. The German name, *Adventsengel mit Flöte*, means "Advent Angel with Flute." The original painting done by Sister Hummel is owned by Ars Edition who used this drawing to publish graphic replicas.

173/0 Festival Harmony with Flute, *new style, TMK-5.*

174 She Loves Me, She Loves Me Not

Indicator	Size	Status	TMK-1	TMK-2	TMK-3	TMK-4	TMK-5	TMK-6
174	4¼"	D,a	300	—	—	—	—	—
174	4¼"	D,b	—	225	175	150	—	—
174	4¼"	P,c	—	—	—	—	76	69

(a – eyes open (up), no flower on post. b – eyes open (up), flower on post. c – eyes closed (down), no flower on post.)

Issued in the 1940s, this piece was modified before 1956 and again in the late 1960s. A premium is included in the TMK-1 price for the early model with a straight-ahead stare and no blossom midway up the upright post on the left side. The TMK-2 version has a very prominent feather in the cap, a flower blossom about midway up the post on the viewer's left, and a straight-ahead gaze. Sometime after 1967, the piece was restyled so that the boy looks down at a smaller daisy. At one time, this piece was listed as "Boy Sitting Before Fence." The German name, *Liebt mich, liebt mich nicht,* is the same as the English.

174 She Loves Me, She Loves Me Not, *eyes down, TMK-5.*

175 Mother's Darling

Indicator	Size	Status	TMK-1	TMK-2	TMK-3	TMK-4	TMK-5	TMK-6
175.	5½"	D,a	325	—	—	—	—	—
175	5½"	D,a	300	240	175	—	—	—
175	5½"	P,b	—	—	125	105	90	84

(a – pink and green bags. b – both bags are light blue.)

This model was called "Happy Harriet" in a late 1940s catalog. The German name, *Markt-Christel,* means "Market, Christine." The earlier TMK-3 examples had no polka dots in the head kerchief; also, the kerchief in her right hand had a pink background with blue polka dots, while the one in her left hand was a light green color wih red polka dots. Furthermore, the polka dots in her dress had a touch of gold in them. The newer TMK-3 version has similar pastel blue backgrounds for each kerchief and white polka dots in the one on her head. This figurine is pictured for the April 1971 calendar page.

175 Mother's Darling, *new colors, TMK-5.*

176　Happy Birthday

176 Happy Birthday, *TMK-5.*

Indicator	Size	Status	TMK-1	TMK-2	TMK-3	TMK-4	TMK-5	TMK-6
176/0	5½"	P	—	210	135	110	96	90
176(.)	5½"	D	500	350	—	—	—	—
176/I	6"	R	450	300	—	—	140	130

When first issued, this figurine was incised either 176 (only) or 176. (decimal), about 5½" high. A Crown mark example shows the girl's forefinger away from her mouth and raised polka dots in her dress. Both girls' shoes are the same shade of brown in this TMK-1 piece. When the smaller 5½" high size was incised 176/0, on an oval base, the larger size was incised 176/I. The larger 176/I was sparsely produced until it was reintroduced in the 6" size in Germany in 1978. Ars Edition, owner and publisher of the original drawing, has issued a cropped version of it as print H 283.

177　School Girls

177 School Girls, *TMK-5.*

Indicator	Size	Status	TMK-1	TMK-2	TMK-3	TMK-4	TMK-5	TMK-6
177	9½"	D	1,800	1,600	1,500	—	—	—
177/I	7½"	P	—	—	700	625	550	500
177/III	9½"	D,a	—	—	1,450	1,400	1,300	1,250

(a – in the Spring of 1982, Goebel announced that Hum. 176/III had been discontinued.)

This group of three girls was introduced in the late 1940s as "Masterpiece" which is the translation of its German name, *Meisterstück*. Examples have been found incised both 177 (only) and 177. (decimal) in TMK-1. One interesting piece in TMK-2 was found marked 177/0. In 1959 it was listed as a special order item, 9¾" high. A smaller size, 7½" high, was copyrighted in the U.S. on December 20, 1961 (GF54). From that time on it was incised 177/I, while the larger size was incised 177/'III instead of only 177. On March 14, 1973, copyright was registered in the U.S. for restyling of 177/III, the larger size. These are found incised 1972, possibly the year of the German copyright. Ars Edition publishes print H 197 from the original drawing in their possession.

178　The Photographer

178 The Photographer, *TMK-5.*

Indicator	Size	Status	TMK-1	TMK-2	TMK-3	TMK-4	TMK-5	TMK-6
178	5"	P	325	180	140	125	110	100

Some examples of the figurine are found incised with the year 1948. The piece was available only as a special order item. The U.S. copyright was registered on July 14, 1950. Other sizes due to mold variations are known. Like so many others, Hum. 178 was redesigned in the 1960s with brighter and shinier colors and minor modifications. Ars Edition owns the original drawing and has produced graphic H 260 from it. See *Hummel Art II,* page 174, for variations between TMK-2, 3, and 5.

　Key to Symbols: A — Assigned; C — Cancelled; D — Discontinued; O — Open; P — Produced; R — Reissued; (?) Examples Doubtful; (—) Examples Unlikely.

179 Coquettes

Indicator	Size	Status	TMK-1	TMK-2	TMK-3	TMK-4	TMK-5	TMK-6
179.	5″	D	350	—	—	—	—	—
179	5″	P	325	225	140	125	110	100

An early catalog from the 1950s lists this as "Coquettes" (two girls on a fence in which there are holes for flowers). It is found in all trademarks and also incised as 179. (decimal) with a Crown mark. One variation has the girl on the viewer's right wearing a dark blue dress and holding flowers. This piece was also restyled and is found brighter and shinier in newer marks. The figurine was pictured in the March 1976 calendar. The German name *Zaungäste* translates as "Fence Guests." The original drawing is owned by Ars Edition and is published as print H 308.

179 Coquettes, *TMK-5.*

180 Tuneful Good Night, Plaque

Indicator	Size	Status	TMK-1	TMK-2	TMK-3	TMK-4	TMK-5	TMK-6
180	5″	R,a	350	275	200	—	100	90
180	5″	D,b	700	—	—	—	—	—

(a – blue dress, tan shoes. b – very light blue dress, blue shoes.)

As with many other plaques, this heart-shaped piece was very infrequently listed in U.S. or bilingual catalogs. Ones with old marks are scarce and relatively high-priced. In 1978 the plaque was reintroduced in the German catalog, and since 1980 it has been listed in the U.S. catalogs. The prices shown above may vary depending on how many new marks are released by Goebel. In an early 1950 catalog this was listed as "Girl Sitting in a Heart." Some of the TMK-5 examples having the painted year "79" on them may also attain collectors' special status. The German name is *Wandschmuck in Herzform, sitzendes Kind mit Trompete,* or in English, "Heart-shaped Wall Ornament, Seated Child with Trumpet." The original drawing has been reproduced as print H 331 by Ars Edition.

180 Tuneful Good Night, *Plaque, TMK-1, no copyright date. Miller Collection.*

181 Old Man Reading Newspaper (CN)

Indicator	Size	Status	TMK-1	TMK-2	TMK-3	TMK-4	TMK-5	TMK-6
181	6¾″	C	*	—	—	—	—	—

This figurine is a faithful adaptation of one of Sister Hummel's caricatures. The original drawing is now owned by Verlag Emil Fink who has published it as lithograph 657. As might be expected from a student, Berta Hummel sometimes drew caricatures to amuse her schoolmates. The figurine is listed in Goebel's records as a closed number as of 1948. For further information see Hum. 189, 190, and 191.
* Only known example is valued in the low five-digit figures.

181 Old Man Reading Newspaper, *prototype, incised M. I. Hummel, no trademark. Miller Collection.*

182 Good Friends, *TMK-5.*

183 Forest Shrine, *rare TMK-2, 9" high.*

184 Latest News, *TMK-5.*

182 Good Friends

Indicator	Size	Status	TMK-1	TMK-2	TMK-3	TMK-4	TMK-5	TMK-6
182.	4"	D	300	—	—	—	—	—
182	4"	P	250	180	110	90	85	79

At one time, this was called "Friends." This model was changed to eliminate confusion with Hum. 136. Throughout the 1950s, this piece was not listed in many of the catalogs, but since that time it has been consistently shown. It was recently restyled by Gerhard Skrobek, Goebel's master modeler, with a more attractive facial expression and with Skrobek's characteristic sculptured hair and textured finish. The German name *Mädchen mit Böckchen* means "Girl with Kid." the original drawing is owned by Ars Edition and issued as graphic H 205.

183 Forest Shrine

Indicator	Size	Status	TMK-1	TMK-2	TMK-3	TMK-4	TMK-5	TMK-6
183	9"	R	1,200	800	500	—	280	260

Always a very scarce collectors' item, this figurine was not listed in U.S. catalogs for years until 1978. It had been considered discontinued by collectors. It was reintroduced first in 1977 in Germany in very limited quantities. In 1980, U.S. catalogs listed the figurine for $260, but it was in very short supply. The reissued examples can be distinguished by the matt or dull finish on the doe, while the ones with early trademarks had a shiny, glossy finish. The German name *Waldandacht, Marterl* means approximately the same as the English. The original drawing has been used by the owner, Ars Edition, as print H 273.

184 Latest News

Indicator	Size	Status	TMK-1	TMK-2	TMK-3	TMK-4	TMK-5	TMK-6
184	5"	D,a	400	300	250	—	—	—
184	5"	D,b	550	450	350	—	—	—
184	5"	D,c	500	400	300	—	—	—
184	5"	D,d	—	500	—	—	—	—
184	5"	P,e	—	—	—	140	120	100

(*a – common titles* (Das Allerneueste, *etc.*), *square base.* *b – unusual titles* (Daily Mail), *with square base.* *c – many other titles in between, square base.* *d – Bermuda News, square base.* *e – present titles, round base.*)

A collector's dream since the 1940s. This model has been issued with a variety of different titles on the newspaper, some of which are very scarce or unique. *Das Allerneueste,* meaning "The Latest News," appears on some. Collectors Bob and Ann Wilgus have this figure reading eleven different newspapers. Redesigned in the 1960s, the current figurine is now on a round base with the boy looking down at the left-hand page. Formerly the base was square and the boy was peering over the top of the paper at the viewer. The original drawing, owned by Ars Edition, has been used to publish graphic H 245.

185 Accordion Boy

Indicator	Size	Status	TMK-1	TMK-2	TMK-3	TMK-4	TMK-5	TMK-6
185	5″	P	230	150	85	80	75	69
185.	5½″	D	250	—	—	—	—	—

Issued in the late 1940s, several early catalogs list this as "On Alpine Pasture," a variation of the German, *Bandoneonspieler,* or "Accordion Player." In a 1950 price list, this piece was about 5½″ high. There are other variations and minor deviations of color, style, and size which do not affect the prices listed above.

185 Accordion Boy, *TMK-5.*

186 Sweet Music

Indicator	Size	Status	TMK-1	TMK-2	TMK-3	TMK-4	TMK-5	TMK-6
186	5″	D,a	800	—	—	—	—	—
186.	5″	D,b	275	200	—	—	—	—
186	5″	P,c	240	140	95	90	85	79

(*a – striped slippers, rare. b – plain slippers. c – standard trademarks and design.*)

It was called "Playing to the Dance" in at least two catalogs in the 1950s. This piece aparently was restyled to incorporate the newer, deeper colors as opposed to the old matt finish. The German name is *Zum Tanz,* or "To the Dance." See *Hummel Art II* for the motif designed in 1956.

186 Sweet Music, *TMK-3.*

187 M.I. Hummel Display Plaques

Indicator	Size	Status	TMK-1	TMK-2	TMK-3	TMK-4	TMK-5	TMK-6
187	4″	D,a	—	—	—	—	1,000	—
187	3¾″	D,b	650	500	400	350	—	—
187	3¾″	D,c	—	—	300	—	—	—
187	3¾″	D,d	—	—	250	—	—	—
187	3¾″	D,e	—	—	—	—	100	—
187	4″	D,f	—	—	—	—	70	—
187A	4″	P,g	—	—	—	—	60	40

(*a – Austrailian, see page 106 of Hummel Art II. b – perched bumblebee. c – large stylized mark with raised circle. d – large stylized mark in oval plaque. e – TMK-5 on oval plaque, copyright 1947. f – TMK-5 on oval plaque, copyright 1976. g – TMK-6 on oval plaque, copyright 1976.*)

See Hum. 205, 208, 209, 210, and 213, for related plaques in other languages and English. The earliest one was issued in the late 1940s and carries a 1947 copyright. The early issue can be distinguished by the large bumblebee sitting on the top facing the Merry Wanderer figurine at the right. In the 1960s, it was replaced with the newly adopted Stylized Bee trademark (TMK-3). The Goebel Bee trademark was introduced in 1972 (TMK-5) for the TMK-3 design. Plain "Goebel" is found on TMK-6. These later plaques are incised with a 1976 copyright date. Variations include a multitude of color combinations. The most personalized is the Australian TMK-5 plaque with the dealer's name. The latest design plaque is now available for purchase by collectors. It is incised 187 A on the back and omits the words "Authorized Dealer."

187 Hummel Display Plaque *with bee on top, TMK-2. Miller Collection.*

188 Celestial Musician, *TMK-5.*

188   Celestial Musician

Indicator	Size	Status	TMK-1	TMK-2	TMK-3	TMK-4	TMK-5	TMK-6
188	7″	P	400	260	200	140	120	110

This piece does not appear in all early catalogs even though it carries a 1948 incised copyright date. It was first copyrighted in the U.S. on July 14, 1950. The size has been listed as 7″ high throughout its history and there is no indication that this figurine has been restyled. The German name *Himmlische Kläge* means "Heavenly Sounds." Robert Miller reports that Hum. 188 was sold in white overglaze at one time. One such example would be rare and valued in the low four-digit figures. Ars Edition owns the original drawing and has used it to publish a faithful replica, H 441.

189   Old Woman Knitting (CN)

Indicator	Size	Status	TMK-1	TMK-2	TMK-3	TMK-4	TMK-5	TMK-6
189	6¾″	C	*	—	—	—	—	—

Perhaps the sum total of Sister Hummel's artwork can be divided into three broad categories: children, religious, and the little-known caricatures (cartoons or humorous exaggerations). Both the first two groups are well represented in the current line of M.I. Hummel figurines. Only the third classification is missing from the Goebel production line, mainly because the convent felt that the caricatures were not representative of Sister Hummel's love of children and her religious dedications, but rather indicated a lighter side of her artistic work. When Goebel submitted four adaptations of her originals in figurine form, Hum. 181, 189, 190, and 191, in the late 1940s, apparently after Sister Hummel's death, the convent did not approve the designs. Robert Miller discovered these four figurines and his research revealed that only samples were made for submission. They should be and probably are insured for values in the five-digit range. The original drawings are owned by Verlag Emil Fink who has published graphics in the form of postcards of these four subjects as 657, 658, 655, and 656.
* Only known example.

189 Old Woman Knitting, *only example, incised M. I. Hummel, no trademark. Miller Collection.*

190   Old Woman Walking to Market (CN)

Indicator	Size	Status	TMK-1	TMK-2	TMK-3	TMK-4	TMK-5	TMK-6
190	6¾″	C	*	—	—	—	—	—

See Hum. 181 and Hum. 189 for information about this group of four similar figurines representing unusual caricatures by Sister Hummel.
* Only known example.

190 Old Woman Walking to Market, *only example, incised M. I. Hummel, no trademark. Miller Collection.*

191 Old Man Walking to Market (CN)

Indicator	Size	Status	TMK-1	TMK-2	TMK-3	TMK-4	TMK-5	TMK-6
191	6¾"	C	*	—	—	—	—	—

See Hum. 181 and Hum. 189 for information about this group of similar figurines.
* Only known example.

191 Old Man Walking to Market, *only example, incised M. I. Hummel, no trademark. Miller Collection.*

192 Candlelight, Candleholder

Indicator	Size	Status	TMK-1	TMK-2	TMK-3	TMK-4	TMK-5	TMK-6
192	7"	D,a	500	400	300	—	—	—
192	6¾"	P,b	—	—	—	80	70	65

(a – long candleholder to angel's feet. b – short candleholder.)

This model was copyrighted in Germany in 1948 and registered in the U.S. on July 14, 1950. At that time, the red ceramic candleholder in the angel's hands extended through her hands, almost to the tip of her shoe. Sometime after 1960 the figure was redesigned so that the candleholder was shortened to a red ceramic socket held in the angle's two hands. It was added again to one U.S. catalog in 1980. The original drawing owned by Ars Edition was lithographed and is listed in their current catalog as H 412. The German name *Engle mit Kerze, Leuchter* translates as "Angel with Candle, Candleholder."

192 Candlelight, *Candleholder, TMK-5.*

193 Angel Duet, Candleholder

Indicator	Size	Status	TMK-1	TMK-2	TMK-3	TMK-4	TMK-5	TMK-6
193	5"	P	320	180	120	100	86	80

The name Angel Duet has also been assigned to a very similar figurine, Hum. 261, which features these same two angels holding a common hymnbook, but no candle. The German copyright date is 1948. Earlier models may be found oversized since they were cataloged in the 1950s as 5½" high. These would be valued at 10 percent more. Robert Miller reports that this model was made at one time in a plain white overglaze which is considered extremely rare. The German name of *Stille Nacht, Engelgrüppchen, Leuchter* translates as "Silent Night, Small Group of Angels." Sister Hummel's original drawing of this motif is owned by Ars Edition and listed in their current catalog as H 411.

193 Angel Duet, *Candleholder, TMK-4. (See Hum. 261.)*

194 Watchful Angel

Indicator	Size	Status	TMK-1	TMK-2	TMK-3	TMK-4	TMK-5	TMK-6
194	6½"	P	550	275	200	160	140	130

This model has had numerous names such as the above, plus "Angelic Care" and "Guardian Angel," and has been found in sizes ranging from about 6½" to over 7½" high with TMK-2. The interchanging of names between models of religious figures is a problem for collectors. One solution is to always accompany any name with the incised number. Many of these are found with a 1948 date incised which represents the German copyright date. *Schutzengel,* the German name, means "Guardian Angel." Print H 436 which is a lithograph from Sister Hummel's original, is available from Ars Edition.

194 Watchful Angel, *copyright 1948, TMK-5.*

195 Barnyard Hero

Indicator	Size	Status	TMK-1	TMK-2	TMK-3	TMK-4	TMK-5	TMK-6
195/2/0	4"	P	200	150	100	85	75	69
195.	5¾"	D	500	—	—	—	—	—
195	5¾"	D	450	—	—	—	—	—
195/I	5½"	P	400	240	180	150	130	120

This piece was first issued with a 1948 incised copyright date, probably in the early 1950s in the U.S. It was available only in one size, 5½" high. Sometime later, the smaller size was introduced, 4" high, incised 195/2/0; at that time 195/I became the indicator for the larger size. In the early models of the smaller size, the boy's hands are on each side of the top rail. When this was restyled, probably in the 1960s, the boy's hands were placed one on top of the other. Sister Hummel's original drawing is owned by Ars Edition and issued as H 158.

Maria from Terri from German
7/83

195/1 Barnyard Hero, *copyright 1948, TMK-5.*

196 Telling Her Secret

Indicator	Size	Status	TMK-1	TMK-2	TMK-3	TMK-4	TMK-5	TMK-6
196/0	5"	P	—	250	200	150	135	120
196.	6½"	D	700	—	—	—	—	—
196	6½"	D	650	550	—	—	—	—
196/I	6½"	R	450	350	300	275	250	230

Copyrighted in the U.S. on July 14, 1950, as "Her Secret," this item carries an incised 1948 copyright date. Although never cataloged, 196/I may have been produced in limited quantities. This vacuum was remedied with the reintroduction of the large 6½" size in 1978. The listed prices for the older marks may be vulnerable to the issue of large quantities of the new pieces with TMK-5 and 6. More documentation is needed on some trademarks. The girl on the right appears alone as Which Hand, Hum. 258. The German name is *Das Geheimnis,* or "The Secret" in English. Sister Hummel's original drawing is owned by Ars Edition and has been issued as print H 291, while the figurine itself has been pictured for the month of February in the 1980 calendar.

196/0 Telling Her Secret, *copyright 1948, TMK-5.*

197 Be Patient

Indicator	Size	Status	TMK-1	TMK-2	TMK-3	TMK-4	TMK-5	TMK-6
197/2/0	4¼″	P	—	135	105	90	80	74
197.	6¼″	D	450	325	—	—	—	—
197	6¼″	D	400	300	—	—	—	—
197/I	6″	P	350	200	150	125	110	100

197/I **Be Patient**, *copyright 1948, TMK-4.*

This little girl feeding ducks is incised with the year 1948. When first issued, the figurine was incised 197 only with TMK-1 and has also been reported incised 197. (decimal) with TMK-2. At that time, only the 6¼″ size was available. This designation was superseded some years later by the designation 197/I to distinguish it from the second size that was issued about 4½″ high and incised 197/2/0. One was reported with a pink apron, TMK-4, 4½″ high. More research is required before establishing premiums on such variations. The German name *Entenmütterchen* translates as "Little Duckling Mother." The location of the original drawing has not been determined.

198 Home from Market

Indicator	Size	Status	TMK-1	TMK-2	TMK-3	TMK-4	TMK-5	TMK-6
198/2/0	4½″	P	—	100	75	65	58	53
198.	5¾″	D	350	225	—	—	—	—
198	5¾″	D	275	200	—	—	—	—
198/I	5½″	P	—	175	130	105	94	84

198/I **Home from Market**, *copyright 1948, TMK-5.*

When this piece was registered in the U.S. in 1950, it was assigned the name "Lucky Buyer." When first issued, it was incised 1948. One piece marked 198/I was found in the Full Bee (TMK-2). The German name *Glück auf, Junge mit Schweinchen in Korb* translates in part as "Happy Purchase" in English. The present location of the original drawing by Sister Hummel is unknown.

199 Feeding Time

Indicator	Size	Status	TMK-1	TMK-2	TMK-3	TMK-4	TMK-5	TMK-6
199/0	4¼″	P	—	180	125	105	90	80
199.	5½″	D	450	—	—	—	—	—
199	5½″	D	400	250	—	—	—	—
199/I	5½″	P	350	200	140	115	100	90

199/I **Feeding Time**, *copyright 1948, TMK-5.*

It was first incised 199 (only) on the bottom, some with Double Crowns, and was about 5½″ tall. The girl had light golden hair. The smaller size was designated by an incised 199/0 on the bottom. Sometime in the early 1960s these were redesigned with a more alert expression, auburn colored hair, rougher surface texture, and brighter colors. The German name *Im Hühnerhoff* translates as "In the Chicken Run." One original Sister Hummel drawing is owned by Ars Edition who uses it to produce print H 236. To date, two original drawings of the Feeding Time design are known.

200 Little Goat Herder

Indicator	Size	Status	TMK-1	TMK-2	TMK-3	TMK-4	TMK-5	TMK-6
200/2/0	4″	D,a	—	400	—	—	—	—
200/0	4¾″	D,b	300	150	—	—	—	—
200/0	4¾″	P,c	—	—	120	100	85	79
200	5½″	D,d	400	300	—	—	—	—
200/I	5½″	D,d	300	275	—	—	—	—
200/I	5½″	P,c	—	—	140	115	100	90

(a – small goat, blade of grass. b – medium goat, blade of grass. c – no grass, copyright 1948. d – large goat, blade of grass.)

200 Little Goat Herder, *new style, TMK-5.*

The copyright date found on some examples is 1948. This figurine was incised 200 (only) or 200. (decimal) on the bottom when first issued in the large 5½″ size. This marking was changed to 200/I a few years later when a smaller 4″ size was introduced and marked 200/2/0. The early model has what was known as a "piece of grass" between the hind legs of the kid in the foreground. This was probably eliminated in a restyling in the 1960s. The German name of *Ziengenhub* means "Goatboy" in English. The original drawing by Sister Hummel has been issued as H 235 by Ars Edition who owns the original.

201 Retreat to Safety

Indicator	Size	Status	TMK-1	TMK-2	TMK-3	TMK-4	TMK-5	TMK-6
201/2/0	4″	P	—	145	100	85	75	69
201.	5¾″	D	450	350	—	—	—	—
201	5¾″	D	400	300	—	—	—	—
201/I	5½″	P	375	220	175	150	132	120

201/2/0 Retreat to Safety, *TMK-5 (see 210).*

The German name is *In tausend Ängsten,* or "With a Thousand Fears." It was originally issued only in the large 5¾″ size and incised with only the whole number 201. When this model was restyled, the boy's hands were placed one on top of the other, whereas before each was placed on either side of the top rail. On some examples 1948 is incised. Ars Edition owns the original drawing by Sister Hummel and publishes graphic H 158.

202 Old Man Reading Newspaper, Table Lamp (CN)

Indicator	Size	Status	TMK-1	TMK-2	TMK-3	TMK-4	TMK-5	TMK-6
202	?	C	—	—	—	—	—	—

A sample of this lamp was made in the late 1940s but was not approved by the convent. Therefore, Hum. 202 was entered as a Closed Number (CN) in the factory records in 1948. See Hum. 181, 189, 190 and 191 for more background information.

203 Signs of Spring

Indicator	Size	Status	TMK-1	TMK-2	TMK-3	TMK-4	TMK-5	TMK-6
203/2/0	4″	D,a	600	500	—	—	—	—
203/2/0	4″	P,b	—	125	100	85	75	69
203	5¼″	D	450	350	—	—	—	—
203	5¼″	D	400	300	—	—	—	—
203/I	5½″	P	—	180	135	115	100	90

*(a – with two shoes. b – with only the left shoe. **Note:** All others have two shoes.)*

This was first incised with the whole number 203 on the bottom of the base, or in some cases 203. (decimal). A change in design in the smaller size was instituted by removing her right shoe so that, today, examples with TMK-2 are found with and without a shoe. This piece was also copyrighted in the U.S. as GP4387 on January 23, 1950, and on December 19, 1977. The German name *Frühlingsidyll* translates as "Spring Idyll."

203/2/0 Signs of Spring, *one shoe, current model, copyright 1948, TMK-4.*

204 Weary Wanderer

Indicator	Size	Status	TMK-1	TMK-2	TMK-3	TMK-4	TMK-5	TMK-6
204	6″	P	325	180	110	100	90	84

The German title *In Lauterbach hab i...* implies that a tired young girl is starting to tell of her long trip to the town of Lauterbach. "Tired Traveler" was the name assigned at the time the copyright was issued to Goebel in the U.S. on July 14, 1950. The figurines are incised 1949. Older catalogs show that the size specifications changed from time to time. A well-known collector has reported a very rare version of the model with blue rather than the usual brown eyes. This blue-eyed piece would be valued at about 100 percent more than the model with brown eyes.

204 Weary Wanderer, *copyright 1949, TMK-5.*

205 Hummel Display Plaque in German

Indicator	Size	Status	TMK-1	TMK-2	TMK-3	TMK-4	TMK-5	TMK-6
205	4″	D	850	750	700	—	—	—

The large bumblebee on top of this plaque suggests that it was issued in the late 1940s to serve as an indication in a store window or counter that M.I. Hummel articles were available for sale. It is similar in contour to the one in English, Hum. 187 (refer to this for more background). Like the Hum. 187 series of plaques, the coloring of the lettering varied as did the style of lettering in some cases. According to the factory records this plaque was closed out in 1949, so the variations are limited. The availability of these plaques to collectors is also limited, as indicated by the high prices for TMK-1, 2, and 3.

205 Hummel Display Plaque, *German, old style, scarce, TMK-1.*

206 Angel Cloud, Holy Water Font

Indicator	Size	Status	TMK-1	TMK-2	TMK-3	TMK-4	TMK-5	TMK-6
206.	4¾"	D	375	—	—	—	—	—
206	4¾"	R	350	300	200	60	30	22

In German the name is *Kind auf wolke,* or "Child with Flower." The name "Angel Cloud" was assigned at the time this design was copyrighted in the U.S. on July 14, 1950. Some fonts are incised with the German copyright date of 1949. It may have been produced in Germany on occasions, but was not listed in early U.S. catalogs. It was reintroduced in the U.S. in 1978 with TMK-5 at a small fraction of the old prices. It is unlikely that the high prices for early trademarks will remain at the present level if many of the newer ones are marketed.

206 Angel Cloud, *Holy Water Font, TMK-2. Hadorn Collection.*

207 Heavenly Angel, Holy Water Font

Indicator	Size	Status	TMK-1	TMK-2	TMK-3	TMK-4	TMK-5	TMK-6
207	4¾"	P	110	50	35	30	25	22

This universally recognized design attained its renown when it was used in bas-relief form on the First Annual Plate, Hum. 264. Both of these bas-reliefs are adapted from the earlier figurine, Heavenly Angel, Hum. 21. (See 21 for more detailed information and background.) When this font was redesigned, probably in the 1960s, the blind hole in the back for hanging was replaced by the pierced hole at the top of the present pieces. This piece resembles H 444 published by Ars Edition, who owns one of the original drawings by Sister Hummel from which this font was adapted.

207 Heavenly Angel, *Holy Water Font, no trademark, copyright 1965. Dous Collection.*

208 Hummel Display Plaque in French

Indicator	Size	Status	TMK-1	TMK-2	TMK-3	TMK-4	TMK-5	TMK-6
208	4"	D	—	7,000	—	—	—	—

A notation in the U.S. copyright records indicates this plaque was copyrighted as early as 1947 and has the large bumblebee sitting on top. This out-of-production plaque is considered very rare as it was never made in large quantities. The scarcity is indicated by the high price. Variations in lettering and punctuation have been reported, but any such variations would fall within the indicated price range already mentioned. There are not that many known.

208 Hummel Display Plaque, *French, old style, rare, TMK-1.*

209 Hummel Display Plaque in Swedish

Indicator	Size	Status	TMK-1	TMK-2	TMK-3	TMK-4	TMK-5	TMK-6
209	4"	D	—	3,000	—	—	—	—

The large bumblebee on top indicates that this piece was probably designed and issued in the late 1940s. No copyright records were found in the U.S. Copyright Office. This was issued for Swedish dealers to display in their store windows or on their counters and is considered very rare. There were at least three plaques that changed hands in 1979, but to date there is insufficient information on design and color variations, if any. It is quite likely that there are fewer than ten of these known, even with all the publicity and high prices.

209 Hummel Display Plaque,
*Swedish, old style, rare, TMK-1.
Grande Collection.*

210 Hummel Display Plaque in English

Indicator	Size	Status	TMK-1	TMK-2	TMK-3	TMK-4	TMK-5	TMK-6
210	4"	D	—	10,000	—	—	—	—

This differs from the other English language plaque, Hum. 187, in one unique respect. Embossed on the Merry Wanderer's satchel are the words "Schmid Bros., Inc., Boston." It was specifically made for this firm which was the first firm to import M.I. Hummel figurines into the U.S. in 1935. The plaque was probably not made before the late 1940s. For more information on the story of M.I. Hummel's introduction into the U.S., refer to the chapter about Berta Hummel art by Schmid Bros. in *Hummel Art II.*

210 Hummel Display Plaque,
*English, Schmid, very rare, TMK-2,
1949 copyright. Artist's simulation.*

211 Hummel Display Plaque in English

Indicator	Size	Status	TMK-1	TMK-2	TMK-3	TMK-4	TMK-5	TMK-6
211	4"	D	—	9,000	—	—	—	—

Another version of the early design of the store window or counter plaque for M.I. Hummel dealers. Why this separate and similar version was made has not been determined. It can be distinguished easily from the other two "big bee" plaques, Hum. 187 and Hum. 210, by the lettering which is done in lowercase rather than uppercase and by the name of the town .Oeslau, where the Goebel figurine factory is located. One sample of this plaque was reported in white overglaze finish. The one pictured here is from the Miller collection and may be one of the only two known.

211 Hummel Display Plaque,
*English, rare, TMK-2. Miller
Collection.*

213 Hummel Display Plaque,
Spanish, rare, TMK-2, 1955 copyright.
Miller Collection.

187 Hummel Display Plaque,
TMK-5, rare Australian version
personalized with dealer's name,
"Carmosino's."

214/A Virgin Mary and Infant
Jesus, *discontinued one-piece figurine.*
Miller Collection.

212   Cancelled Number

Indicator	Size	Status	TMK-1	TMK-2	TMK-3	TMK-4	TMK-5	TMK-6
212	—	C	—	—	—	—	—	—

According to factory records there is no information available on a design or sample with this number, and it is classified as a Closed Number (CN) never to be used again. Robert Miller, in *HUMMEL, Authorized Supplement*, believes that this may have been intended for grouping a number of existing, related figurines and selling them under Hum. 212 as an orchestra.

213   Hummel Display Plaque in Spanish

Indicator	Size	Status	TMK-1	TMK-2	TMK-3	TMK-4	TMK-5	TMK-6
213	4"	D	—	9,000	—	—	—	—

Another in the series of the big bumblebee plaques, probably designed in the late 1940s. This plaque is one of three that used lowercase letters instead of capitals in the wording on this long-discontinued, old style.

214   Nativity Set (Small)

Indicator	Size	Status	TMK-1	TMK-2	TMK-3	TMK-4	TMK-5	TMK-6
Nativity Set (12 pc.,c)								
214	2"–7"	P	—	900	825	780	750	675
Nativity Set (12 pc.,w)								
214	2"–7"	D	—	2,500	2,000	1,750	—	—
Nativity Set (16 pc.,c)								
214	2"–7"	P	—	1,100	1,050	1,000	950	855
Nativity Set (16 pc.,w)								
214	2"–7"	D	—	2,750	2,250	2,000	—	—
Nativity Set (2 pc.,c)								
214M/K&B	7"	D,a	—	2,500	1,750	—	—	—
Nativity Set (3 pc.,c)								
214 AMBK	7"	P	—	400	300	225	195	184
Mary and Infant (1 pc.,c)								
214/A	6¼"	D,b	—	2,200	—	—	—	—
Mary and Infant (2 pc.,c)								
214 AMK	6¼"	P	—	200	175	150	120	106
Infant only (c)								
214 A/K	1½"	P	—	50	40	35	30	26
St. Joseph (c)								
214/B	7½"	P	—	150	125	100	90	79
Goodnight (c)								
214/C	3½"	P	—	70	55	50	40	37
Angel Serenade (c)								
214/D	3"	P	—	60	45	40	36	32
We Congratulate (c)								
214/E	3½"	P	—	120	90	80	70	63
Shepherd Standing (c)								
214/F	7"	P	—	160	130	105	95	84
Shepherd Kneeling (c)								
214/G	4¾"	P	—	100	80	70	65	57

Little Tooter (c)								
214/H	4"	P	—	90	75	60	55	48
Donkey (c)								
214/J	5"	P	—	55	45	40	35	30
Cow (c)								
214/K	3½"	P	—	55	45	40	35	30
Moorish King (c)								
214/L	8"	P	—	150	125	100	90	79
King Kneeling, one knee (c)								
214/M	5½"	P	—	150	125	100	90	79
King Kneeling (c)								
214/N	5½"	P	—	150	125	90	80	75
Lamb (c)								
214/O	2"	P	—	25	20	15	10	9
Flying Angel (c)								
366	3½"	P	—	—	—	70	60	53
Flying Angel								
366	3½"	P	—	—	—	25	21	19

(c – color. w – white glaze. a – madonna and child in one piece with Joseph added. b – madonna and child in one piece. Note: Old individual white pieces TMK-2, add 150 percent to color price; in TMK-3, TMK-4 add 100 percent to color prices.)

Many ardent M.I. Hummel collectors have one of these sets which is the focal point of their Christmas decorations and just as essential as the tree. Others buy these figurines piecemeal at a rate of one a year. Some of the pieces are incised with a 1951 date. One set is known to have been purchased in Buffalo, New York, just prior to Christmas, 1949, with a TMK-2, or Full Bee trademark. Over the years, the individual pieces have not always been available, but now are. The latest addition, the sixteenth piece, is Flying Angel, Hum. 366, which was added in the mid-1970s. At present, the stable is not included in the sixteen pieces and is sold separately for $50. It is also currently offered as a twelve-piece set which omits the following: 214/C Angel Standing ("Goodnight"); 214/D Angel Kneeling ("Angel Serenade"); 214/E We Congratulate; and 214/H Shepherd Boy Kneeling ("Little Tooter"). Sometimes a camel, marked HX306/0/6 because it was not designed by Sister Hummel, is available as an extra piece. The Nativity Set was once offered in an all-white finish and when found is a collector's item.

214 Nativity Set with Stable, *TMK-3. (214/C, 214/O not pictured.) A similar nativity set made by Goebel is not incised M.J.Hummel. It is incised HX-257 and sells for much less. Check carefully before buying.*

215   Cancelled Number

Indicator	Size	Status	TMK-1	TMK-2	TMK-3	TMK-4	TMK-5	TMK-6
215	—	C	—	—	—	—	—	—

Two sources indicate different subjects were considered for this number, but apparently were never made. The number was classed as a Closed Number (CN) in 1951. Factory records indicate it was considered for a design of the Child Jesus. The U.S. Copyright Office lists a copyright on November 5, 1964, for the design of a Madonna in Prayer as number 215.

216   Cancelled Number

Indicator	Size	Status	TMK-1	TMK-2	TMK-3	TMK-4	TMK-5	TMK-6
216	—	C	—	—	—	—	—	—

According to Goebel's factory records, this number was being considered for a variation of Joyful, Ashtray, Hum. 33, but for some unknown reason it was listed as a Closed Number (CN) in 1951.

217   Boy with Toothache

Indicator	Size	Status	TMK-1	TMK-2	TMK-3	TMK-4	TMK-5	TMK-6
217	5½"	D,a	—	175	150	—	—	—
217	5½"	P,b	—	140	105	88	80	74

(a – light blue coat. b – dark blue coat.)

This was first found in an early 1950s catalog as 5" high and with an incised copyright date of 1951. During World War II, a poor quality reproduction of this called "Dentist Dodger" or "Bawling Bennie" was issued by Dubler in the U.S. The original drawing by Sister Hummel, issued by Ars Edition as H 257, shows this bandaged boy standing at the dentist's office pulling a bellcord to announce his arrival. There are two known copies of this drawing. Sister Hummel made a second one for her dentist in Saulgau.

217 Boy with Toothache, *TMK-4.*

218   Birthday Serenade

Indicator	Size	Status	TMK-1	TMK-2	TMK-3	TMK-4	TMK-5	TMK-6
218/2/0	4¼"	P,a	—	—	—	95	85	74
218/2/0	4¼"	D,b	—	400	350	275	—	—
218/0	5¼"	R,a	—	—	—	—	132	120
218	5¼"	D,b	—	700	—	—	—	—
218/0	5½"	P,b	—	575	475	375	—	—

(a – present design, girl with horn. b – old design, boy with horn.)

An interesting change in design was made in this pair for unexplained reasons in about 1965. The boy playing the horn was switched to playing the accordion, and the girl did the reverse, going from the accordion to the horn. Old design pieces are incised 1952, even including the newly reintroduced pieces, Hum. 218/0 with the TMK-5 and 6 (in error), which now also have the boy playing the accordion and the girl playing the horn. Other new pieces with the girl playing the horn are incised 1965. In making this change, the boy also acquired a slightly askew scarf around his neck.

218/2/0 Birthday Serenade, *new design, TMK-5.*

219   Little Velma

Indicator	Size	Status	TMK-1	TMK-2	TMK-3	TMK-4	TMK-5	TMK-6
219/2/0	4″	D	—	4,000	—	—	—	—

This is a figurine named by the authoritative collector, Robert Miller, in honor of the woman who first identified it. Previous research indicated that this figurine, "Girl with Frog," might have been made in very small quantities but for some reason was discontinued. The number 219 was incorrectly listed as a Closed Number (CN) and never used. Even the U.S. Copyright Office record is incomplete. However, it does describe it as "Girl on Fence with Frog." As of now, somewhere between five and ten pieces of this extremely rare model have been reported. A woman in Canada whose son had purchased Hum. 219 for her with $5 he earned on his newspaper route in the 1950s recently received about the price shown above.

219/2/0 Little Velma, *rare, TMK-2. Dous Collection.*

220   We Congratulate

Indicator	Size	Status	TMK-1	TMK-2	TMK-3	TMK-4	TMK-5	TMK-6
220/2/0	4″	D	—	200	—	—	—	—
220	4″	P	—	130	100	85	75	68

This figurine is essentially the same as the other ones by the same name, Hum. 214/E and Hum. 260 F, in the Nativity Sets, except that a base was added and two changes were made in design. The garland of flowers has been omitted from the girl and suspenders have been added to the boy. The year 1952 is incised on some models. When first issued, the model number was incised 220/2/0. Later, the size indicator was omitted. Therefore present models carry only the number 220. This has not been reported in a white overglaze finish like Hum. 214/E.

220 We Congratulate, *on base (see 214/E), TMK-5.*

221   Happy Pastime, Candy Box (CN)

Indicator	Size	Status	TMK-1	TMK-2	TMK-3	TMK-4	TMK-5	TMK-6
221	?	C	—	—	—	—	—	—

According to Robert Miller's *HUMMEL, Authorized Supplement,* this number was originally listed as "Unknown," as factory records indicated it as a Closed Number (CN). Hum. 221 was planned at one time to be a glamorized version of the present Candy Box, Hum. III/69. The main difference was the addition of flowers and blossoms on the top and sides of the box which would have been very vulnerable to damage. The bird was also positioned in front of the girl and her kerchief was without polka dots. This additional information is given in case you are the fortunate collector to have the only one known, other than the factory sample. It should be insured for a few thousand dollars.

222 Madonna Plaque, Wire Frame

Indicator	Size	Status	TMK-1	TMK-2	TMK-3	TMK-4	TMK-5	TMK-6
222	5"	D	—	750	600	—	—	—

This is based on a popular painting by Sister Hummel entitled "Madonna in Red." Verlag Emil Fink has published lithographic prints in a number of different versions. Originally, Hum. 222 had an ornate black metal strap frame. So far this has only been reported with TMK-2 and 3. Complete, the value would be as above. Without the frame, about 25 percent less if incised Hum. 222, 4" x 5". Ars Edition has a similar Madonna, H 533.

222 **Madonna Plaque,** *wire frame, discontinued, TMK-2. Miller Collection.*

223 To Market, Table Lamp

Indicator	Size	Status	TMK-1	TMK-2	TMK-3	TMK-4	TMK-5	TMK-6
M223	9½"	P	—	450	400	300	275	230

This lamp is based on the figurine, To Market, Hum. 49, and is closely related to two other lamps, Hum. 101 and Hum. II/101, which should be referred to for more background. The principal difference between this lamp and the other two lamps is in size. Hum. 223 is 9½" as compared to 7½" for the other two. This also has a blossom on the tree trunk which II/101 does not have. The German name, *Brüderlein and Schwesterlein,* means "Brother and Sister," which these two figurines are called when they are listed separately as Hum. 95 and Hum. 98.

223 **To Market,** *Table Lamp, trademark unknown.*

224 Wayside Harmony, Table Lamp

Indicator	Size	Status	TMK-1	TMK-2	TMK-3	TMK-4	TMK-5	TMK-6
M224	9½"	D	—	475	—	—	—	—
M224/I	7½"	P	—	300	250	200	185	170
M224/II	9½"	R	—	360	300	250	220	210

This adaptation of the figurine Hum. 111, by the same name, was apparently first issued incised only 224, 9½" high. The 9½" size was perhaps an alternative to Hum II/111, the same lamp in the 7½" size. In the 1950s, Hum. 224/I replaced the smaller, 7½" size lamp. Concurrently, the markings on the 9½" lamp were changed to 224/II. Hum. 224/II has been intermittently available in the U.S. market but was not cataloged by distributors until it was reintroduced in 1978.

224 **Wayside Harmony,** *Table Lamp, trademark unknown.*

225 Just Resting, Table Lamp

Indicator	Size	Status	TMK-1	TMK-2	TMK-3	TMK-4	TMK-5	TMK-6
M225		D	—	475	—	—	—	—
M225/I	7½″	P	—	300	250	200	185	170
M225/II	9½″	R	—	360	300	250	220	210

An ideal companion piece to Wayside Harmony Lamp, Hum. 224, over the years this model has had much the same history of size, number, and size indicator changes. Hum. 225/II, also, has been infrequently available on the U.S. market, and was not cataloged by distributors until it was reintroduced in 1978.

225 Just Resting, *Table Lamp,* *TMK-5.*

226 The Mail Is Here

Indicator	Size	Status	TMK-1	TMK-2	TMK-3	TMK-4	TMK-5	TMK-6
226	6″	P	—	450	400	350	275	250

This popular piece was originally copyrighted in the U.S. as "Stage Coach" in 1954. Most of the pieces are incised as 1952. Some of the early catalogs also list this as "Mail Coach." The German name *Trara-die Post ist da* translates in English as "Ta-dum, the Mail Is In." One original drawing is owned by Ars Edition. The other is in the Kleber Post Inn in Saulgau. Sometimes Sister Hummel waited at this inn to go to the nearby convent in Siessen. This drawing shows the coach from the rear as it is leaving the inn with a tearful woman waving her handkerchief out of the back window. Displayed together they make a very interesting pair. Graphic by Ars Edition is H 617.

226 The Mail Is Here, *copyright* *1952, TMK-4.*

227 She Loves Me, She Loves Me Not, Table Lamp

Indicator	Size	Status	TMK-1	TMK-2	TMK-3	TMK-4	TMK-5	TMK-6
M227	7½″	D,a	—	400	300	—	—	—
M227	7½″	P,b	—	—	—	200	175	160

(a – eyes open. b – eyes closed.)

This lamp and its companion piece, Hum. 228, Good Friends, were made only in this 7½″ size. This adaptation of figurine, Hum. 174, has a flower on the left fencepost and eyes looking up (or straight at the viewer) in TMK-2 and 3. Eyes closed or looking down are found in TMK-4, 5, and 6.

227 She Loves Me, She Loves Me Not, *Table Lamp, TMK-5.*

228 Good Friends, *Table Lamp,*
TMK-5.

229 Apple Tree Girl, *Table Lamp,*
7½" high, TMK-5. Miller Collection.

230 Apple Tree Boy, *Table Lamp,*
7½" high, TMK-5. Miller Collection.

228 Good Friends, Table Lamp

Indicator	Size	Status	TMK-1	TMK-2	TMK-3	TMK-4	TMK-5	TMK-6
M228	7½"	P	—	300	230	200	175	160

Like its companion piece, Hum. 227, this lamp has been made only in the 7½" size since its introduction in the 1950s. This lamp also was listed as being 8½" high in the same 1959 catalog (no doubt in error) and would be valued about 25 percent more if found that large. Neither Hum. 227 nor Hum. 228 is known to date with the earlier Crown mark, TMK-1. Refer to the figurine of the same name, Hum. 182, for more information. Good Friends was matched with She Loves Me as one of a pair of Bookends, Hum. 251 A.

229 Apple Tree Girl, Table Lamp

Indicator	Size	Status	TMK-1	TMK-2	TMK-3	TMK-4	TMK-5	TMK-6
M229	7½"	P	—	300	230	200	175	160

This well-known figurine is a natural for a lamp because the girl is already sitting in the branches of a tree. Introduced about 1955 in the 7½" size, it was listed in a 1959 catalog as being 8½" high, but an 8½" lamp has yet to be found. This same model is also used in one of the pair of Bookends, Hum. 252A. There is no record of this having been made in the larger 9½" size as some other lamps have been. Refer to the figurine, Hum. 141, Apple Tree Girl, for more information.

230 Apple Tree Boy, Table Lamp

Indicator	Size	Status	TMK-1	TMK-2	TMK-3	TMK-4	TMK-5	TMK-6
M230	7½"	P	—	300	230	200	175	160

The same information applies to this lamp as previously detailed for Hum. 229. This model was also used as part of the Bookends, Hum. 252 B, and the 1977 Annual Plate, Hum. 270, the year after the girl was used on a similar plate, Hum. 269. Both lamps, Hum. 229 and Hum. 230, were copyrighted in the U.S. in 1955, and both pieces are known in TMK-2 through TMK-6. See Hum. 142 for more information on Apple Tree Boy.

231 Birthday Serenade, Table Lamp

Indicator	Size	Status	TMK-1	TMK-2	TMK-3	TMK-4	TMK-5	TMK-6
M231	9½″	D,a	—	1,500	—	—	—	—
M231	9½″	R,b	—	—	—	1,000	255	230

(a – TMK-2, boy playing horn. b – reissue, girl playing horn.)

This lamp places the same musicians who comprise the Birthday Serenade figurine, Hum. 218, at the base of a tree trunk which forms the lamp standard. The lamp was known only in TMK-2. In 1978, Hum. 231 was reintroduced with a TMK-5; however, one collector owns an example with a TMK-4. The TMK-2 lamps are incised with a 1954 copyright date. Refer to Hum. 218 for full details on the change in design made in the mid-1960s at the request of the convent. Hum. 234, a lamp similar to Hum. 231, differs slightly in size and design. The lamp was considered rare until the reissue appeared in 1978. The price differential between old and new models may change.

231 **Birthday Serenade,** *Table Lamp, 9½″ high, TMK-5. Miller Collection.*

232 Happy Days, Table Lamp

Indicator	Size	Status	TMK-1	TMK-2	TMK-3	TMK-4	TMK-5	TMK-6
M232	9½″	R,a	—	1,200	—	—	250	230

(a – early TMK-2 lamps are rare; reissued version in 1978.)

This 9½″ high table lamp utilized the figurine by the same name, Hum. 150. The early models are incised with a 1954 copyright date. At present, any examples of this lamp with a TMK-3 or TMK-4 would also be considered unusual. No listing for this lamp was found until it was reissued in 1978 in Germany and later in other countries. The TMK-2 examples were considered rare and usually sold as indicated above. The price of these may drop based on the number of reissues produced. The large 9½″ lamp is practically identical to the companion 7½″ model, Hum. 235. The German name for this lamp is *Hausmusik, Kinderpaar,* which translates as "House Music by Pair of Children."

232 **Happy Days,** *Table Lamp, 9½″ high, TMK-5. Miller Collection.*

233 Cancelled Number

Indicator	Size	Status	TMK-1	TMK-2	TMK-3	TMK-4	TMK-5	TMK-6
233	?	C	—	—	—	—	—	—

Gerhard Skrobek, who is currently the master sculptor for Goebel, started to work there in 1954. In Robert Miller's *HUMMEL, Authorized Supplement,* Miller states that Hum. 233 was the first assignment Skrobek had of interpreting one of Sister Hummel's drawings as a figurine. The figurine was listed at that time in the factory records as being a boy feeding birds. For unknown reasons, it was never produced and not even a factory sample or original study has been reported.

234 Birthday Serenade, Table Lamp

234 Birthday Serenade, *Table Lamp,*
7½" high, TMK-2. Miller Collection.

Indicator	Size	Status	TMK-1	TMK-2	TMK-3	TMK-4	TMK-5	TMK-6
M234	7½"	D,a	—	1,500	1,200	1,000	—	—
M234	7½"	R,b	—	—	—	—	253	230

(a – boy plays horn, rare. b – reissue, girl plays horn.)

This 7½" lamp is the smaller version of Hum. 231, with the older models carrying an incised 1954 copyright date. The 7½" version varies from the 9½" version in that it has no flower in the branch stub above the boy's head. It was reissued in Germany in 1978. Early models of the lamp were considered scarce and commanded a premium price. Early models are identified by the boy playing the horn and the girl the accordion. When reissued in 1978, the motif was restyled so that the boy plays the accordion and the girl the horn. The English name is the same as the German, *Geburtstagsstandchen.*

235 Happy Days, Table Lamp

235 Happy Days, *Table Lamp,*
TMK-2, copyright 1954. Miller
Collection.

Indicator	Size	Status	TMK-1	TMK-2	TMK-3	TMK-4	TMK-5	TMK-6
M235	7½"	D,a	—	1,200	800	—	—	—
M235	7½"	R,b	—	—	—	—	225	200

(a – TMK-2, rare, discontinued. b – reissued in 1978, TMK-5 and 6.)

Happy days, Hum. 150, is essentially the same design that was used for this smaller 7½" size, and for Hum. 232, the 9½" size, except that the larger model has a flower hanging down over the boy's head. Refer to Hum. 218 and Hum. 150 for more information. The date of the incised copyright year on the bottom is 1954. The new reissued version in 1978 may adversely affect the prices of the older, scarce models. The German name for this lamp is *Hausmusik, Kinderpaar,* which translates as "House Music by Pair of Children," which is also the German name of the figurine, Hum. 150.

236 Open Number

Indicator	Size	Status	TMK-1	TMK-2	TMK-3	TMK-4	TMK-5	TMK-6
236		O	—	—	—	—	—	?

A previous publication distributed by the Goebel Company indicates that this number was never assigned to one of Sister Hummel's drawings for adaptation into a three-dimensional object. Thus, number 236 remains available for assignment.

237 Cancelled Number

Indicator	Size	Status	TMK-1	TMK-2	TMK-3	TMK-4	TMK-5	TMK-6
237	?	C	—	—	—	—	—	—

The factory classified this number as "a number which has not been used and will not be used to identify 'M.I. Hummel' figurines," until Robert Miller conducted more research at the factory. It was then discovered that at one time this number was assigned to a wall plaque named "Star Gazer." This might have been an intended adaptation of Hum. 132, Star Gazer, to add to the growing group of wall plaques. Hope should spring eternal in the heart of the avid collector that she or he may be the one destined to uncover the only example of 237 ever made.

238 Angel Trio (B) (Set)

Indicator	Size	Status	TMK-1	TMK-2	TMK-3	TMK-4	TMK-5	TMK-6
238/A	2½"	P	—	—	—	28	25	22
238/B	2"	P	—	—	—	28	25	22
238/C	2½"	P	—	—	—	28	25	22

238 A, B, C Angel Trio (B) Set. *TMK-4, 1967 copyright. Miller Collection.*

This Hummel number is used for three different, seated angels which are distinguished by the letter suffix, A, B, or C. "A" plays the lute (banjo); "B" plays the accordion; and "C" plays the trumpet. Almost every expert still gets the similar small figurines mixed up. These angels are incised with the copyright date 1967, which coincides with the three U.S. copyrights issued in December of 1967. They must have been released about that time. So far these have only been found with TMK-4, 5, 6. These are usually sold as a set and priced in that manner.

239 Children Trio (A) (Set)

Indicator	Size	Status	TMK-1	TMK-2	TMK-3	TMK-4	TMK-5	TMK-6
239/A	3½"	P	—	—	—	30	27	24
239/B	3½"	P	—	—	—	30	27	24
239/C	3½"	P	—	—	—	30	27	24

239 A, B, C Children Trio (A) Set.

239 A Girl with Nosegay, *TMK-5.*

239 B Girl with Doll, *TMK-5.*

239 C Boy with Horse, *TMK-5.*

This group's name and number are used for three different figures cataloged and sold either as a set or individually. These are incised with a 1967 copyright date on the bottom of the bases and were registered in the U.S. on December 19, 1967. So far they have only been found with the last three trademarks, TMK-4, 5, and 6. The three children have been adapted from Advent Candlesticks, Hum. 115, 116, and 117. Refer to *Hummel Art II*, page 214, "Mel" figurines.

240   Little Drummer

Indicator	Size	Status	TMK-1	TMK-2	TMK-3	TMK-4	TMK-5	TMK-6
240	4¼″	P	—	95	80	65	58	53

This figurine is listed in some catalogs as "Drummer," which agrees with the German name *Trommler.* These models are incised 1955. So far no significant variations in conformation or color have been reported, although there are minor variations in height from the currently specified size of 4¼″. It was not listed in a widely circulated, multilingual catalog of 1956; however, it was found listed under the name "Drummer," 4½″ high, in a 1957 U.S. catalog.

240 Little Drummer, *copyright 1955, TMK-5.*

241   Angel Joyous News with Lute, Font (CN)

Indicator	Size	Status	TMK-1	TMK-2	TMK-3	TMK-4	TMK-5	TMK-6
241		C	—	—	—	—	—	—

241   Angel Lights, Candleholder

Indicator	Size	Status	TMK-1	TMK-2	TMK-3	TMK-4	TMK-5	TMK-6
241 B	8⅜″	P	—	—	—	—	150	135

241 B Angel Lights, *Candleholder, TMK-5. Introduced in 1978; number assigned in error.*

No one expected that this number would be used for the release of M.I. Hummel 241. It was introduced into the Hummel line in 1978 and was first called "Angel Bridge." This was changed to the present name, Angel Lights, when it was found that another item made by Goebel had already used that name. These should be purchased in this complete form. Originally, Hum. 241 was assigned to Font Angel, Joyous News with Lute, produced as a sample, only. It is possible that Goebel will assign a new number to Angel Lights.

242   Cancelled Number

Indicator	Size	Status	TMK-1	TMK-2	TMK-3	TMK-4	TMK-5	TMK-6
242	?	C	—	—	—	—	—	—

This number was initially assigned for an adaptation of Joyous News, Angel with Trumpet in the manner of either Hum. 27, Hum. 40, or Hum. 238 C. According to Robert Miller, only a sample was made and the number was cancelled in 1955. Since examples of similar cancelled numbers have shown up in the past few years (see Hum. 77), there is always the remote possibility that one or more of these will be discovered.

243 Madonna and Child, Holy Water Font

Indicator	Size	Status	TMK-1	TMK-2	TMK-3	TMK-4	TMK-5	TMK-6
243	4"	P	—	40	32	28	25	22

Examples of this font are incised with a copyright date of 1955. Since there is no record to date of an example with TMK-1, it must have been introduced shortly after the copyright date. However, distribution was very limited since no old U.S. or international catalogs available had this piece listed. The 1969 Hummelwerk catalog is the earliest U.S. listing found. This appears similar in style to Sister Hummel's well-known "Madonna in Red." The German name, *Madonna un Kind*, translates as "Madonna and Child."

243 Madonna and Child, *Holy Water Font, TMK-4.*

244–245 Open Numbers

Indicator	Size	Status	TMK-1	TMK-2	TMK-3	TMK-4	TMK-5	TMK-6
244	O		—	—	—	—	—	?
245	O		—	—	—	—	—	?

According to Goebel factory records, these numbers were never assigned for adaptation as figurines or other art form. This being the case, they have been listed as open numbers over the years and may at some future time be assigned to new Hummel products by the Goebel Company.

246 Holy Family, Holy Water Font

Indicator	Size	Status	TMK-1	TMK-2	TMK-3	TMK-4	TMK-5	TMK-6
246	4"	P	—	45	37	32	28	25

While this font carries an incised copyright date of 1955, it was copyrighted in the U.S. on April 27, 1956, as GP12631 with the name "Madonna with Jesus and Joseph." The font is found in all trademark periods except in the Crown period. The first available catalogs that list Hum. 246 are dated 1959; thereafter, this font seems to have been called "Holy Family." Verlag Emil Fink published it as postcard 210.

246 Holy Family, *Holy Water Font, TMK-5.*

247 Standing Madonna with Child, *sample only, courtesy of W. Goebel Co.*

247 Standing Madonna, (CN)

Indicator	Size	Status	TMK-1	TMK-2	TMK-3	TMK-4	TMK-5	TMK-6
247	13″	C	*	—	—	—	—	—

In earlier publications, including *Hummel Art I*, Hum. 247 was listed as a Closed Number which would never be used again. Thanks to some dedicated research by Robert Miller, we now know that this number was used for a standing madonna. The tall (13″) figurine, adapted from a painting by Sister Hummel, carried the provisional name "Standing Madonna and Child." She is distinguished from other madonnas by the star-topped crown and the rosary draped over her left arm.
*Factory sample only.

248 Guardian Angel, *Holy Water Font, TMK-4.*

248 Guardian Angel, Holy Water Font

Indicator	Size	Status	TMK-1	TMK-2	TMK-3	TMK-4	TMK-5	TMK-6
248	5½″	P	—	?	—	—	25	22
248/0	5½″	D	—	—	100	50	—	—
248/I	6¼″	D	—	—	600	—	—	—

This design was first copyrighted in the U.S. on February 17, 1959, and is incised "1959" on the back of each piece. It apparently was issued about this time since it is found with TMK-3 through TMK-6. One unverified report claims an example with TMK-2. This piece modified a similar font by the same name, Hum. 29, which was discontinued in the late 1950s. For Hum. 248, the angel's wings are made an integral part of her head in order to strengthen them. It is now listed and marketed only in the smaller size which is incised 248 (only).

249 Madonna and Child, *Plaque, rare, designed by Skrobek, TMK-2, courtesy W. Goebel Co.*

249 Madonna and Child, Plaque (CN)

Indicator	Size	Status	TMK-1	TMK-2	TMK-3	TMK-4	TMK-5	TMK-6
249	8¾″	C	—	*	—	—	—	—

When *Hummel Art I* was published in 1978, there was no information available on this model. It was listed as a Closed Number which would never be used again. Careful research of the company archives by Robert Miller revealed an unusual wall plaque of the "Madonna in Red," as Hum. 249. It differs from all other known wall plaques except Hum. 263, Merry Wanderer. It is simply a bas-relief of the motif without any background mounting.
*Factory sample only.

250 A   Little Goat Herder, Bookend

Indicator	Size	Status	TMK-1	TMK-2	TMK-3	TMK-4	TMK-5	TMK-6
250/A	5½"	P	—	—	235	200	175	160

250 A&B Little Goat Herder, Feeding Time, *Bookends. TMK-5.*

Prices shown are for the pair, both 250 A and B. This half of a pair of bookends was produced by taking the figurine Little Goat Herder, Hum. 200, and securing it to a wooden base with a simulated slat fence for the book rest. The identification and trademark are shown on the wooden base because the base of the figurine is not visible. The restyled version of the figurine was used for this bookend. These bookends are normally found with TMK-3 through TMK-6.

250 B   Feeding Time, Bookend

Indicator	Size	Status	TMK-1	TMK-2	TMK-3	TMK-4	TMK-5	TMK-6
250/B	5½"	P	—	—	235	200	175	160

Prices shown are for the pair, both 250 A and B. The figurine, Hum. 199, is permanently secured on a wooden base as described under Hum. 250 A. The two are usually cataloged as 250 A and B and now sold only as a pair. See 250 A for remarks about trademarks.

251 A   Good Friends, Bookend

Indicator	Size	Status	TMK-1	TMK-2	TMK-3	TMK-4	TMK-5	TMK-6
251/A	5"	P	—	—	235	200	175	160

251 A&B Good Friends, She Loves Me, *trademark unknown. Miller Collection.*

Prices shown are for the pair, both 251 A and B. Here again is a standard figurine on a ceramic base attached to a wooden base with an upright rest for books. For more details on the figurine itself, see Good Friends, Hum. 182. This pair (251 A and B) was first found in a U.S. catalog dated 1965. Since the figurine was restyled in the mid-1970s, the bookends with TMK-5 and 6 will show the same more modern look and coloring.

251 B   She Loves Me, She Loves Me Not, Bookend

Indicator	Size	Status	TMK-1	TMK-2	TMK-3	TMK-4	TMK-5	TMK-6
251/B	5"	P	—	—	235	200	175	160

Prices shown are for the pair, both 251 A and B. The figurine of the boy picking petals from a daisy forms the other half of this set. The bookends are cataloged and sold as a set. For further details on this portion of the set see the description of the figurine itself, Hum. 174. This half of the set has also been restyled with the boy looking down at a flower rather than with the straight-ahead stare of the earlier models.

252 A&B Apple Tree Girl and Boy, *Bookends, TMK-5.*

252 A Apple Tree Girl, Bookend

Indicator	Size	Status	TMK-1	TMK-2	TMK-3	TMK-4	TMK-5	TMK-6
252/A	5″	P	—	—	235	200	175	160

Prices shown are for the pair, both 252 A and B. This bookend is the small figurine, Hum. 141/3/0, mounted permanently on a wooden base which is incised with all the identification marks. This set was issued about the middle of the 1960s. For more details, refer to Hum. 141. This motif also appears in Table Lamp, Hum. 229, and the 1976 Annual Plate in bas-relief, Hum. 269.

252 B Apple Tree Boy, Bookend

Indicator	Size	Status	TMK-1	TMK-2	TMK-3	TMK-4	TMK-5	TMK-6
252/B	5″	P	—	—	235	200	175	160

Prices shown are for the pair, both 252 A and B. The figurine 142/3/0 is used for the second part of the Hum. 252 bookends. The remarks about Apple Tree Girl are equally applicable to Apple Tree Boy. Refer to Hum. 142 for full information on the history of this motif.

253 Cancelled Number

Indicator	Size	Status	TMK-1	TMK-2	TMK-3	TMK-4	TMK-5	TMK-6
253	?	C	—	—	—	—	—	—

At first it was generally thought that this was a number never used by Goebel, but research by Robert Miller and the factory indicate that it was assigned to the figure of a girl with a basket. There are no known samples at the factory or elsewhere.

254 Cancelled Number

Indicator	Size	Status	TMK-1	TMK-2	TMK-3	TMK-4	TMK-5	TMK-6
254	?	C	—	—	—	—	—	—

Like 253 above, it was an unknown, never to be used, until a search by Robert Miller and factory personnel found it had been assigned to a figure of a girl playing a mandolin. A U.S. copyright in 1963 described the design as that of a girl on a base holding flowers.

255 Stitch in Time

Indicator	Size	Status	TMK-1	TMK-2	TMK-3	TMK-4	TMK-5	TMK-6
255	6¾″	P	—	—	160	120	100	90

Stitch in Time was copyrighted on August 22, 1963, in the U.S. and cataloged by 1965. *Zwei Rechts — Zwei Links,* German for "Two to the right — two to the left," is an active and more specific name for this determined knitter. Her third debut in the line occurs in Knitting Lesson, Hum. 256.

255 Stitch in Time, *copyright 1963, TMK-5.*

256 Knitting Lesson

Indicator	Size	Status	TMK-1	TMK-2	TMK-3	TMK-4	TMK-5	TMK-6
256	7½"	P	—	—	300	260	230	210

This knitter already appeared as one of the trio in School Girls, Hum. 177. Copyrighted in the U.S. on October 9, 1963, Hum. 256 appeared in a 1964 U.S. catalog. The figurine is incised with the year of copyright, 1963. The German name *Ob's gelingt* asks, "Will it work?" To date, no unusual variation in this model has been reported.

256 Knitting Lesson, *copyright 1963, TMK-4.*

257 For Mother

Indicator	Size	Status	TMK-1	TMK-2	TMK-3	TMK-4	TMK-5	TMK-6
257	5"	P	—	—	85	75	65	60

This model was introduced in the U.S. in 1964, the year of the New York World's Fair. There was no record found of a U.S. copyright date. The figurines are incised 1963. This motif was used as the illustration for the month of May in the 1973 calendar. No major changes have been noted to date, but an example with TMK-2 could be a valuable prototype.

257 For Mother, *copyright 1963, TMK-5.*

258 Which Hand?

Indicator	Size	Status	TMK-1	TMK-2	TMK-3	TMK-4	TMK-5	TMK-6
258	5½"	P	—	—	85	75	65	60

This model appeared in Telling Her Secret, Hum. 196. The U.S. copyright was issued in August of 1963, the year incised on the figurine, and cataloged in 1964. So far no major changes have been reported in style or color. The German name of *Rat mal!* translates to "Guess!" Graphics of the original work of Sister Hummel are cataloged by Ars Edition as H 291. The figurine appeared in the October 1973 calendar.

258 Which Hand? *Copyright 1963, TMK-5.*

259 Cancelled Number

Indicator	Size	Status	TMK-1	TMK-2	TMK-3	TMK-4	TMK-5	TMK-6
259	?	C	—	—	—	—	—	—

Research of the factory records within the last few years has revealed that this number was assigned to the design "Girl with Accordion." The project was cancelled in 1962 with no known examples.

260 A-R Large Nativity Set,
TMK-5.

260 Nativity Set (Large)

Indicator	Size	Status	TMK-1	TMK-2	TMK-3	TMK-4	TMK-5	TMK-6
Nativity Set (16 pc. with stable)								
260		P	—	—	—	3,000	2,780	2,525
Madonna								
260/A	9¾"	P	—	—	—	338	310	279
Saint Joseph								
260/B	11¾"	P	—	—	—	338	310	279
Infant Jesus								
260/C	5¾"	P	—	—	—	70	65	58
Goodnight								
260/D	5¼"	P	—	—	—	90	80	72
Angel Serenade								
260/E	4¼"	P	—	—	—	80	70	63
We Congratulate								
260/F	6¼"	P	—	—	—	230	210	189
Shepherd Standing								
260/G	11¾"	P	—	—	—	360	330	300
Sheep with Lamb								
260/H	3¾"	P	—	—	—	65	60	53
Shepherd Kneeling								
260/J	7"	P	—	—	—	200	180	166
Little Tooter								
260/K	5⅛"	P	—	—	—	100	90	80
Donkey								
260/L	7½"	P	—	—	—	80	70	63
Cow								
260/M	11"	P	—	—	—	100	90	80
Moorish King								
260/N	12¾"	P	—	—	—	340	310	279

Indicator	Size	Status	TMK-1	TMK-2	TMK-3	TMK-4	TMK-5	TMK-6
King Standing								
260/O	12″	P	—	—	—	340	310	279
King Kneeling								
260/P	9″	P	—	—	—	315	285	260
Sheep Lying								
260/R	3¼″	P	—	—	—	35	30	26

This set was copyrighted in 1968 in the U.S. Consisting of sixteen pieces, the figurines bear suffix letters from A through R. The pieces are about 50 percent larger than those in Nativity Set, Hum. 214. Pieces are priced and sold individually as shown. This set is not listed in all catalogs. Hum. 260/F, We Congratulate, has no base, while figurine, Hum. 220, does.

261 Angel Duet

Indicator	Size	Status	TMK-1	TMK-2	TMK-3	TMK-4	TMK-5	TMK-6
261	5″	P	—	—	—	105	95	84

This modified version of Hum. 193 (Candleholder) with the identical name confuses many collectors. The differences are that in Hum. 261 the candle socket has been eliminated and the position of one angel's arm has changed. The angel on the viewer's right has his left hand holding the hymnbook and his right hand encircling the other angel's waist. In Hum. 193, the angel on the viewer's right does not hold the hymnbook and holds the candleholder in his left hand.

261 Angel Duet *(see 193)*, TMK-5. *Miller Collection.*

262 Heavenly Lullaby

Indicator	Size	Status	TMK-1	TMK-2	TMK-3	TMK-4	TMK-5	TMK-6
262	5″	P	—	—	250	90	80	75

Another example of a candleholder modified into a figurine using the same figures as Lullaby, Hum. 24. It is approximately the same size as the smaller Hum. 24/I which is 3½″ × 5″, but is incised with the copyright date of 1968. It is found in limited quantities marked TMK-3 through TMK-6. The German name *Wiegenlied* means "Lullaby."

262 Heavenly Lullaby, *TMK-5.*

263 Merry Wanderer, Plaque

Indicator	Size	Status	TMK-1	TMK-2	TMK-3	TMK-4	TMK-5	TMK-6
263	5″	C	—	—	*	—	—	—

This was considered a Closed Number which had never been assigned and never would be used. Robert Miller and the Goebel Company found that Hum. 263 was a style of wall plaque of the very popular Merry Wanderer for which two wall plaques already existed, Hum. 92 and Hum. 106. However, both Hum. 92 and Hum. 106 have frames. Hum. 263 is a bas-relief of the figure itself with a flat back and a slot for hanging. The only known example is a factory sample.
*Factory sample only.

263 Merry Wanderer Plaque, *sample only, courtesy of W. Goebel Co.*

264 Annual Plate, 1971, Heavenly Angel, *TMK-4. Courtesy W. Goebel Co.*

264 Reverse of 1971 Annual Plate. *"1871-1971.*
IN COMMEMORATION OF THE 100TH ANNIVERSARY OF W. GOEBEL-HUMMELWERK. W. GERMANY."
Courtesy W. Goebel Co.

264   Annual Plate 1971, Heavenly Angel

Indicator	Size	Status	TMK-1	TMK-2	TMK-3	TMK-4	TMK-5	TMK-6
264	7½"	C,a	—	—	—	1,000	—	—
264	7½"	C,b	—	—	—	750	—	—

(a – special inscription on workers' copies of these plates. b – the limited number issued accounts for the increase over issue price.)

The Goebel Company completed its first century in business in 1971. In order to commemorate this event and to recognize the employees' contribution to its continued success, the company issued a special plate — a bas-relief design of Heavenly Angel matching the figurine, Hum. 21. On the back of the plate was an inscription acknowledging the employees' contribution to the Goebel Company. One of these was given to each person employed (several thousand in all). In addition, the plate without this special inscription was offered for general sale (issue price $25 in the U.S.) during that year with the mold destroyed at the end of the year. A transfer-decorated plate with the Heavenly Angel design was introduced by the Schmid Bros. the same year for $15. The plates received by each employee carried a special inscription. Reports of an occasional one being available have been received.

Three design studies of Annual Plate, 1971, Heavenly Angel, Hum. 264. Design on right was adopted. Factory samples courtesy W. Goebel Co.

265 Annual Plate, 1972, Hear Ye, Hear Ye!

Indicator	Size	Status	TMK-1	TMK-2	TMK-3	TMK-4	TMK-5	TMK-6
265	7½"	C	—	—	—	50	45	—

The second annual issue is a bas-relief replica of the figurine of the same name, Hum. 15. This plate is also 7½" in diameter and has the ring of embossed stars around the outside edge. Since the plate's issue, the trademark was changed from TMK-4 to TMK-5. The Goebel Bee was used until 1979. As a result, plates are found with either trademark. The issue price was $38.

265 Annual Plate, 1972, Hear Ye, Hear Ye!, *TMK-4.*

266 Annual Plate, 1973, Globe Trotter

Indicator	Size	Status	TMK-1	TMK-2	TMK-3	TMK-4	TMK-5	TMK-6
266	7½"	C	—	—	—	—	130	—

The third Annual Plate, 1973, has the bas-relief replica of Globe Trotter, Hum. 79. One minor and unexplained variation is the fact that this plate is the only one to date that has only thirty-two stars in the identifying border. All other years have thirty-three stars. The issue price was $40. Since the new TMK-5 (Goebel Bee mark) was introduced in 1972, this plate is found with the newer TMK-5 marks.

266 Annual Plate, 1973, Globe Trotter, *TMK-5.*

267 Annual Plate, 1974, Goose Girl

Indicator	Size	Status	TMK-1	TMK-2	TMK-3	TMK-4	TMK-5	TMK-6
267	7½"	C	—	—	—	—	70	—

The Goose Girl figurine, Hum. 47, is one of the most identifiable and best known of all M.I. Hummel figurines. The issue price for a 1974 plate that year was $46. Many collectors are buying the figurine to mount in a shadow box frame with the plate itself.

267 Annual Plate, 1974, Goose Girl, *TMK-5.*

268 Annual Plate, 1975, Ride into Christmas

Indicator	Size	Status	TMK-1	TMK-2	TMK-3	TMK-4	TMK-5	TMK-6
268	7½"	C	—	—	—	—	65	—

This fifth Annual Plate utilizes the design of the original figurine by that name, Hum. 396, in bas-relief form. The first copyright was filed on June 22, 1972, and the second one on November 19, 1973. In 1982 a smaller version of the figurine was introduced. The issue price of this new one is $50.

Photographs courtesy W. Goebel Co.

268 Annual Plate, 1975, Ride into Christmas, *TMK-5.*

269 Annual Plate, 1976, Apple Tree Girl, *TMK-5.*

269 Annual Plate, 1976, Apple Tree Girl

Indicator	Size	Status	TMK-1	TMK-2	TMK-3	TMK-4	TMK-5	TMK-6
269	7½"	C	—	—	—	—	65	—

Apple Tree Girl is another favorite that is almost synonymous with M.I. Hummel. The figurine from which the bas-relief was developed is Hum. 141, which is worth referring to for additional background information. The issue price of the 1976 model was $50.

270 Annual Plate, 1977, Apple Tree Boy, *TMK-5.*

270 Annual Plate, 1977, Apple Tree Boy

Indicator	Size	Status	TMK-1	TMK-2	TMK-3	TMK-4	TMK-5	TMK-6
270	7½"	C	—	—	—	—	50	—
270	7½"	C,a	—	—	—	—	100	—

(a – example with uneven socks.)

As expected, Apple Tree Boy, taken from the figurine of the same name, Hum. 142, was used for 1977. Robert Miller reported a variation in the plates for that year. The boy's right sock was made higher than the left one. An early sample shows the left sock longer, with the shoes at a slightly different angle. The issue price was increased to $65.

271 Annual Plate, 1978, Happy Pastime, *TMK-5.*

271 Annual Plate, 1978, Happy Pastime

Indicator	Size	Status	TMK-1	TMK-2	TMK-3	TMK-4	TMK-5	TMK-6
271	7½"	C	—	—	—	—	70	—

These plates were in short supply all that year in the U.S. Many collectors could not get one at the issue price of $65, and had to pay more. The speculators had a major hand in escalating the price. Demand for the companion figurine, Happy Pastime, Hum. 69, also increased.

272 Annual Plate, 1979, Singing Lesson, *TMK-5.*

272 Annual Plate, 1979, Singing Lesson

Indicator	Size	Status	TMK-1	TMK-2	TMK-3	TMK-4	TMK-5	TMK-6
272	7½"	C	—	—	—	—	55	—

Alongside the 1978 Annual Plate, the 1979 Annual Plate is an attractive, almost mirror image design, which makes an attractive pair. The issue price that year was $90. The increase in price coupled with Goebel's expanded production before the end of the year satisfied the needs of most collectors.

Photographs courtesy W. Goebel Co.

273 Annual Plate, 1980, School Girl

Indicator	Size	Status	TMK-1	TMK-2	TMK-3	TMK-4	TMK-5	TMK-6
273	7½"	C	—	—	—	—	—	70

This plate is another Goebel collectors' favorite. The increased price ($100 per plate), Goebel's expanded production, and the U.S. recession kept supply and demand more nearly in balance so that most collectors were able to buy their examples through regular channels at the suggested price.

273 Annual Plate, 1980, School Girl, *TMK-6*.

274 Annual Plate, 1981, Umbrella Boy

Indicator	Size	Status	TMK-1	TMK-2	TMK-3	TMK-4	TMK-5	TMK-6
274	7½"	C	—	—	—	—	—	80

The well-known Umbrella Boy, Hum. 152/A, was selected for adaptation in bas-relief on this plate. The price has been held to $100. With sufficient production available, most collectors have been pleased to find their plates without too much difficulty at regular prices.

274 Annual Plate, 1981, Umbrella Boy, *TMK-6*.

265 Annual Plate, 1982, Umbrella Girl

Indicator	Size	Status	TMK-1	TMK-2	TMK-3	TMK-4	TMK-5	TMK-6
275	7½"	P	—	—	—	—	—	65

This plate is a bas-relief of Hum. 152/B. Goebel, in order to alleviate some of the excessive demand for figurines matching Annual Plates, decided to preannounce the subjects of future Annual Plates through 1986.

275 Annual Plate, 1982, Umbrella Girl, *trademark unknown*.

276 Annual Plate, 1983, Postman

Indicator	Size	Status	TMK-1	TMK-2	TMK-3	TMK-4	TMK-5	TMK-6
276	7½"	A	—	—	—	—	—	?

The figurine of the same name, Hum. 119, has been used for this plate, but portrayed in bas-relief from an attractive side view. The U.S. copyright registration number is GF1077, dated November 19, 1973.

Photographs courtesy W. Goebel Co.

276 Annual Plate, 1983, Postman, *trademark unknown*.

277 Annual Plate, 1984, Little Helper, *trademark unknown.*

277 Annual Plate, 1984, Little Helper

Indicator	Size	Status	TMK-1	TMK-2	TMK-3	TMK-4	TMK-5	TMK-6
277	7½"	A	—	—	—	—	—	?

This bas-relief was derived from the figurine of the same name, Hum. 73. The most notable difference is that the basket has been filled with some appetizing fruit. Sister Hummel's drawing shows round objects in the basket. Refer to Ars Edition graphic H 340, a duplicate of the original drawing.

278 Annual Plate, 1985, Chick Girl, *trademark unknown.*

278 Annual Plate, 1985, Chick Girl

Indicator	Size	Status	TMK-1	TMK-2	TMK-3	TMK-4	TMK-5	TMK-6
278	7½"	A	—	—	—	—	—	?

The figurine derivative chosen for this plate is Hum. 57, with three chicks in the basket. U.S. Copyright GF1075 was issued on November 19, 1973, to cover this plate design.

279 Annual Plate, 1986, Playmates, *trademark unknown.*

279 Annual Plate, 1986, Playmates

Indicator	Size	Status	TMK-1	TMK-2	TMK-3	TMK-4	TMK-5	TMK-6
279	7½"	A	—	—	—	—	—	?

The plate is patterned after the figurine by the same name, Hum. 58; the plate motif follows the design in the larger of the two figurines, 58/I, as the rabbit in the back has both ears up. This last plate in the preannounced future issues was copyrighted on November 19, 1973, as GF1074.

280 Anniversary Plate, 1975, Stormy Weather, *trademark unknown.*

280 Anniversary Plate, 1975, Stormy Weather

Indicator	Size	Status	TMK-1	TMK-2	TMK-3	TMK-4	TMK-5	TMK-6
280	10"	D	—	—	—	—	150	—

To date, the series consists of two plates issued at five-year intervals. The issue price was $100. A comparison of this bas-relief with the figure by the same name, Hum. 71, will immediately indicate a drastic difference in the treatment of the children's expressions. Research indicates that Sister Hummel created two drawings involving these two children. Ars Edition graphic H 287, "Sunny Weather," was used for this plate, Hum. 280. The figurine, Hum. 71, was made from Ars Edition H 288, "Stormy Weather."

Photographs courtesy W. Goebel Co.

281　Anniversary Plate, 1980, Spring Dance

Indicator	Size	Status	TMK-1	TMK-2	TMK-3	TMK-4	TMK-5	TMK-6
281	10"	D	—	—	—	—	—	225

This plate, Hum. 281, is a modification of the figurine, "Spring Dance." The girl on the right is taken from that figurine. The girl on the left appears to have been in the same position on "Ring Around the Rosie," Hum. 348. Actually, the girl on the right appears in both groups.

281 Anniversary Plate, 1980, Spring Dance, *trademark unknown. Courtesy W. Goebel Co.*

282-299　Open Numbers

Indicator	Size	Status	TMK-1	TMK-2	TMK-3	TMK-4	TMK-5	TMK-6
282-299	—	O	—	—	—	—	—	?

Goebel defines an Open Number as "An identification number, which in W. Goebel's numerical identification system has not yet been used, but which may be used to identify new 'M. I. Hummel' figurines as they are released in the future." It is important to remember that over twenty new figurines and articles were copyrighted in 1955 and were not introduced in the U.S. until 1971-1972. These nineteen Hummel numbers from 281 through 299 provide sufficient numbers to cover issues to the year 2000 for the Annual and Anniversary Plate series. Starting with Hum. 300, the next thirty-six numbers were all assigned by the year 1955 or 1956, and should carry copyright dates very close to those years. From Hum. 337 through Hum. 350, all of the U.S. copyrights were registered in 1972. Hum.500 was registered on January 22, 1975, as GF1152 for a 1976 Mother's Day Plate entitled, "Flowers for Mother."

300　Bird Watcher

Indicator	Size	Status	TMK-1	TMK-2	TMK-3	TMK-4	TMK-5	TMK-6
300	5"	P	—	2,500	—	—	105	95

Between an early design in 1956 and its release in the U.S. in 1979 as Bird Watcher, some restyling must have been done. It has the deeply sculpted hair and other earmarks of the more recent work of Skrobek. This small figurine had a suggested issue price of $90, but the demand was so great that within months some dealers were asking as much as $250 for it.

300 Bird Watcher, *issued 1979, TMK-5.*

301 Christmas Angel (Assigned).

301 Christmas Angel (Assigned Number)

Indicator	Size	Status	TMK-1	TMK-2	TMK-3	TMK-4	TMK-5	TMK-6
301	6¼"	A	—	—	—	—	—	?

When this piece was copyrighted in the U.S. in 1958, it was listed as "Delivery Angel with Basket." The Miller collection displayed a sample of this figurine which has a TMK-3, in Eaton, Ohio, in 1980. Hum. 301 will be classed here as an Assigned Number which may be released at some unknown future date. A graphic, H 442, has been published by Ars Edition, who owns the original drawing.

302 Concentration (Assigned). From H 197 courtesy Ars Edition.

302 Concentration (Assigned Number)

Indicator	Size	Status	TMK-1	TMK-2	TMK-3	TMK-4	TMK-5	TMK-6
302	5"	A	—	—	—	—	—	?

This item was originally called "Do It Like Me" (Girl Knitting) when it was copyrighted. The German name *Wie macht sie das nur* translates as "How Does She Do It." When and how the final name, "Concentration," was decided upon is not known. Hum. 302 will be classified as an Assigned Number at present and its status will be changed to "Produced" and "Priced" when and if it is offered for sale.

303 Arithmetic Lesson (Assigned). From H 198 courtesy Ars Edition.

303 Arithmetic Lesson (Assigned Number)

Indicator	Size	Status	TMK-1	TMK-2	TMK-3	TMK-4	TMK-5	TMK-6
303	5¼"	A	—	—	—	—	—	?

This little girl and boy figurine puzzling over a math problem appears to be a combination of the center boy from Hum. 170, School Boys, and the right-hand girl from Hum. 177, School Girls. It is unknown whether Sister Hummel composed such a drawing or whether it was contrived by the Goebel sculptor. This figurine was copyrighted in the U.S. on October 19, 1955. Graphics H 197 and H 198 by Ars Edition may have been the inspiration for this studious pair.

304　The Artist

Indicator	Size	Status	TMK-1	TMK-2	TMK-3	TMK-4	TMK-5	TMK-6
304	5½″	P	—	—	1,500	240	100	90

While this figurine of a boy with a palette was only cataloged for sale in this country in 1971, it is incised with a 1955 copyright date and was registered in the U.S. Copyright Office in that year on October 20. The German name *Kunstmaler* translates as "The Artist Painter." Hum. 304 is found in TMK-3 through TMK-6. One authority considers TMK-4 to be scarce. An early sample with a TMK-3 would be a rare find. A graphic, H 251, has been published by Ars Edition, who owns the Sister Hummel drawing.

304 **The Artist,** *copyright 1955, TMK-5.*

305　The Builder

Indicator	Size	Status	TMK-1	TMK-2	TMK-3	TMK-4	TMK-5	TMK-6
305	5½″	—	—	—	—	150	120	100	90

This figurine of a mason or bricklayer is named more descriptively in German, *Der Schwerarbeiter,* or "The Heavy Worker." Found in TMK-3 through TMK-6, there remains the unlikely possibility that this item will be discovered in TMK-2. Many early catalogs list only "Builder," as do some current catalogs. The location of the original drawing is undetermined at this time and no graphics have been found.

305 **The Builder,** *copyright 1955, TMK-5.*

306　Little Bookkeeper

Indicator	Size	Status	TMK-1	TMK-2	TMK-3	TMK-4	TMK-5	TMK-6
306	4¾″	P	—	2,000	200	115	98	90

This is another motif that was copyrighted in the busy year of 1955 when it was registered in the U.S. on June 19. The copyright year is also incised on the base of the figure. It appeared in catalogs in this country in the early 1960s and is known with TMK-2 through TMK-6. There is no record of any restyling or major variations in color or design to date. Graphic H 202 has been published by Ars Edition.

306 **Little Bookkeeper,** *copyright 1955, TMK-5.*

307 Good Hunting

Indicator	Size	Status	TMK-1	TMK-2	TMK-3	TMK-4	TMK-5	TMK-6
307	5"	P	—	2,000	180	150	100	90

Hum. 307 is another of the introductions in the early 1960s which is often confused with Sensitive Hunter, Hum. 6. Unimportant variations have been reported in TMK-3 through TMK-6. The incised copyright goes back to the year 1955. This could mean that samples were made at this time with TMK-2. The graphic of this was produced by Ars Edition as H 238. The name of this figurine in German is *Weidmannsheil,* meaning "Good Sport."

307 Good Hunting, *copyright 1955, TMK-5.*

308 Little Tailor

Indicator	Size	Status	TMK-1	TMK-2	TMK-3	TMK-4	TMK-5	TMK-6
308	5½"	P,b	—	—	—	—	110	100
308	5½"	D,a		1,200	400	200	—	

(a – 1955 coyright date. b – 1972 copyright date incised.)

This is one of over twenty figurines that were part of the 1955 all-out copyright effort by Goebel. Though the figurines were not introduced until 1972, the incised date sometimes confuses collectors into thinking that 1955 was the year of introduction. This piece is usually found with TMK-4 through TMK-6, although an unverified report was received of one with a TMK-3. The current catalogs list this piece as 5½" high, although variations from this size are known. Ars Edition's graphic from the original is H 258.

308 Little Tailor *(new style), copyright 1972, TMK-5.*

309 With Loving Greetings (Assigned Number)

Indicator	Size	Status	TMK-1	TMK-2	TMK-3	TMK-4	TMK-5	TMK-6
309	3¼"	A	—	—	—	—	—	?

While this was copyrighted under the name "Yours Very Truly" on June 24, 1955, it still remains held in abeyance as an Assigned Number which may be issued at some futured date. The German name of *Ein dicker Gruss* is translated as "A Big Greeting." Sister Hummel's original drawing is owned by Ars Edition, who publishes graphic H 23 from it.

309 With Loving Greetings *(Assigned). From H 623 courtesy Ars Edition.*

310 Searching Angel, Plaque

Indicator	Size	Status	TMK-1	TMK-2	TMK-3	TMK-4	TMK-5	TMK-6
310/A	4¼"	P	—	—	—	—	66	60

First introduced in the U.S. in the January 1979 catalogs, this kneeling angel on a cloud is found with only TMK-5 and TMK-6. In these catalogs and also in Canada, this plaque is listed as Hum. 310 A, indicating the possibility of a 310 B plaque. Some of these pieces carry the artist's painted year, "79," and some do not. This artist's datemark, new in 1979, is favored by some collectors. It is incised 1955 on the back. The present name in German is *Was ist denn do drunten los?* which translates into English as "What's Happening Down Below?" Ars Edition has published graphic H 451 from Sister Hummel's original drawing.

310 Searching Angel, *Plaque, issued 1979, TMK-5.*

311 Kiss Me

Indicator	Size	Status	TMK-1	TMK-2	TMK-3	TMK-4	TMK-5	TMK-6
311	6"	D,a	—	—	400	250	—	—
311	6"	P,b	—	—	—	—	100	90

(a – with socks. b – without socks.)

When copyrighted in 1955 (the date incised on the bottom), the doll wore socks. It was introduced in this form in the early 1960s with TMK-3. The figurine was restyled later in the decade at the request of the Siessen Convent to make the doll appear more "doll-like." At that time, the socks on the doll were omitted. The German name of *Hab'mich lieb!* means "Love Me!" The original drawing by Sister Hummel was reproduced by Ars Edition as graphic H 231.

311 Kiss Me, *with socks, copyright 1955, TMK-5.*

312 Honey Lover (Assigned number)

Indicator	Size	Status	TMK-1	TMK-2	TMK-3	TMK-4	TMK-5	TMK-6
312	3¾"	A	—	—	—	—	—	?

A seated boy, without the usual figurine base, apparently licking honey off his forefinger, is terrified by a large honeybee. It was copyrighted in this country on July 18, 1955, under the assigned name "Honey Licker" or *Honiglecker* in German. This boy may be released at a later date with the trademark then in use. The original drawing by Sister Hummel is owned by Ars Edition, who has published graphic H 116 from the original.

312 Honey Lover *(Assigned). From H 116 courtesy Ars Edition.*

313 Sunny Morning *(Assigned). From H 108 courtesy Ars Edition.*

313 Sunny Morning (Assigned Number)

Indicator	Size	Status	TMK-1	TMK-2	TMK-3	TMK-4	TMK-5	TMK-6
313	3¾"	A	—	—	—	—	—	?

This baby in a crib in front of a fence with a huge overhanging sunflower blossom was assigned this number back in 1955. It was registered in the U.S. Copyright Office as "Sunny Child." When and if it is released, it will carry the trademark current at that time. The German name assigned to this piece is *Sonnenkind* which translates as "Sun Child." In Miller's *HUMMEL, Authorized Supplement,* he says it was also referred to as "Slumber Serenade." To see exactly what the original drawing looks like, see graphic H 108 by Ars Edition.

314 Confidentially *(new style), copyright 1972, TMK-5.*

314 Confidentially

Indicator	Size	Status	TMK-1	TMK-2	TMK-3	TMK-4	TMK-5	TMK-6
314	5½"	D,a	—	1,500	600	400	200	—
314	5½"	P,b	—	—	—	120	100	90

(a – 1955 copyright, no tie. b – 1972 copyright, with tie.)

This figurine, called *Zwiegespräch* in German, and "Dialogue" in English, was designed and copyrighted in the U.S. on October 20, 1955. The original design was shelved from 1955 to 1972. The boy had no bow tie and his hair was smoother. In 1972, when first offered in the U.S., a bow tie had been added. The plant stand now had a low step, and the "Skrobek" sculptured look to the hair. TMK-3 through TMK-6 are available. When introduced in 1972, the price was about $22. Graphic H 254, published by Ars Edition, is an exact replica of the original drawing.

315 Mountaineer, *copyright 1955, TMK-5.*

315 Mountaineer

Indicator	Size	Status	TMK-1	TMK-2	TMK-3	TMK-4	TMK-5	TMK-6
315	5"	P	—	1,500*	200	115	100	90

This satisfied mountain climber says in German *I' hab's erreicht* or "I have achieved it." It is documented in TMK-3 through TMK-6 and was first sold in the U.S. in 1964, the year of the New York World's Fair. If found in an earlier mark, it would be an exception and worth a premium. Reports of a TMK-2 mark have not been sufficiently verified. This is incised 1955. There have been no major variations in design, color, or size reported. A graphic produced from the original art of Sister Hummel has been published by Ars Edition as H 203.
*A prototype.

316 Relaxation (Assigned Number)

Indicator	Size	Status	TMK-1	TMK-2	TMK-3	TMK-4	TMK-5	TMK-6
316	4″	A	—	—	—	—	—	?

Hum. 316 was registered on October 20, 1955, in the U.S. Copyright Office under th name *Sommerfrische,* which is incised on the piece itself and means "Summer Freshness." The figurine has also been referred to as "Nightly Ritual." It is classed as an Assigned Number until approved for distribution at some future date. The German name for this unpublished edition is *Eine gute Erholung,* meaning "A Good Recuperation." Graphic H 162 has been published by Ars Edition, who owns the original drawing.

316 Relaxation *(Assigned). From H 162 courtesy Ars Edition.*

317 Not for You

Indicator	Size	Status	TMK-1	TMK-2	TMK-3	TMK-4	TMK-5	TMK-6
317	6″	P	—	—	200	115	100	90

This is a favorite figurine of dog lovers. Some collectors match this piece with Which Hand, Hum. 258, to make a similar pair. The year incised on the base is 1955. It was listed in catalogs of the early 1960s as 5½″ high when it was first introduced. Presently the specified catalog size is 6″ high. Therefore, variations in size can be expected. The German name for this model is *Nix für dich!* or "Nothing for You." Sister Hummel's original drawing is owned by Ars Edition and has been published as graphic H 292.

317 Not for You, *copyright 1955, TMK-5.*

318 Art Critic (Assigned Number)

Indicator	Size	Status	TMK-1	TMK-2	TMK-3	TMK-4	TMK-5	TMK-6
318	5½″	A	—	—	—	—	—	?

Copyrighted July 18, 1955, in the U.S. as Art Critic, this piece remains, after twenty-five years, an unproduced edition. The motif portrays a young boy with brush in his right hand studying a framed painting held in his left hand, with a blue bottle at his right foot. The assigned German name is *Der Kunstkritiker,* essentially the same as the English translation. When and if this will be produced for sale is unknown and until then it will be classified as an Assigned Number to be issued with the trademark that is being used at that time.

318 Art Critic *(Assigned). From H 252 courtesy Ars Edition.*

319   Doll Bath

Indicator	Size	Status	TMK-1	TMK-2	TMK-3	TMK-4	TMK-5	TMK-6
319	5″	P	—	—	250	120	100	90

This is a very popular M.I. Hummel figurine which is not always available because of demand. The base is incised with the copyright year 1956. It is usually found with TMK-4 through TMK-6. A possible but unlikely occurrence would be an example with a TMK-2, which might indicate that it was an early sample from the mid-1950s. It was published by Verlag Emil Fink as 221 in different sized graphics. The German name *Puppen bad* is the same as the English.

319 Doll Bath, *copyright 1956, TMK-5.*

320   The Professor (Assigned Number)

Indicator	Size	Status	TMK-1	TMK-2	TMK-3	TMK-4	TMK-5	TMK-6
320	5¾″	A	—	—	—	—	—	—

Copyrighted in 1955, over twenty-five years have elapsed since the copyright date. When and if he will ever be issued as an approved member in good standing of the M.I. Hummel entourage is not known. If and when this happens, he will no doubt be distinguished by the trademark in use at the time. Sister Hummel's original drawing of this motif is owned by Ars Edition, who has published an exact duplicate of the original drawing and cataloged it as H 24a.

"Der Professor"

320 The Professor *(Assigned). From H 240 courtesy Ars Edition.*

321   Wash Day

Indicator	Size	Status	TMK-1	TMK-2	TMK-3	TMK-4	TMK-5	TMK-6
321	6″	D,a	—	—	2,500	—	—	—
321	6″	P,b	—	—	300	150	100	90

(a – holding long sheet. b – holding a kerchief.)

At the Eaton Festival in Eaton, Ohio, in June of 1980, an interesting early study sample was displayed alongside the present design. This version, believed to have been designed by Unger in 1955, shows a sheet rather than a handkerchief reaching from the figure's extended hands to the basket. The present model, introduced in the early 1960s at about 6″ high, is holding a much smaller article, perhaps a kerchief. Production pieces are incised with the 1957 date. The German name for this motif is *Grosse Wäsche*, or "Big Wash." The graphic from the original drawing, published by Ars Edition, interestingly pictures her fastening the last clothespin to hang a pair of pants on the line. The catalog number is H 232.

321 Wash Day, *copyright 1957, TMK-4.*

322 Little Pharmacist

Indicator	Size	Status	TMK-1	TMK-2	TMK-3	TMK-4	TMK-5	TMK-6
322	6″	P,a	—	—	350	125	105	95
322	6″	P,b	—	—	300	120	105	95
322	6″	D,c	—	—	—	350	—	—

(a – with vitamins. b – with Rizinusol. c – with castor oil.)

Bearing on incised 1955 copyright date on the base, this pharmacist figurine was listed in U.S. catalogs in the early 1960s in a 6″ size. The bottle he is holding has been found with different labels, the most common being "Vitamins" and the German word for castor oil, *Rizinusol*. Any other factory-applied name would be considered very special. It is found with TMK-3 up to the current mark. Samples made in 1955, if found, would probably have TMK-2 and be considered premium examples valued in the low four-digit figures. The German name, *Der Apotheker*, stands for "The Pharmacist." This motif has been published from the original drawing of Sister Hummel by Ars Edition as graphic H 241.

322 Little Pharmacist, *copyright 1955, TMK-5.*

323 Merry Christmas, Plaque

Indicator	Size	Status	TMK-1	TMK-2	TMK-3	TMK-4	TMK-5	TMK-6
323	5″	P	—	—	—	—	66	60

This small angel was copyrighted in this country on October 7, 1955, and the plaques are incised on the back with the same year. The U.S. copyright lists the name as "Angel on Cloud." The German name is *Frohe Weihnachten*. The 5″ plaque is found only with TMK-5 and TMK-6, since it was first introduced in 1979. Some of the pieces may have the artist's date of "79" brushed on and some may not. As time elapses, a differential may be established in favor of one or the other. The original of this particular drawing is owned by Ars Edition, who published graphic H 437 from it.

323 Merry Christmas, *Plaque, copyright 1955, issued 1979, TMK-5.*

324 At the Fence (Assigned Number)

Indicator	Size	Status	TMK-1	TMK-2	TMK-3	TMK-4	TMK-5	TMK-6
324	?	A	—	—	—	—	—	?

The copyright filed in the U.S. Copyright Office in 1956 describes this as "figures at a fence." It shows two young boys in back of a section of rail fence with a longhaired dachshund on the other side barking at them. This is enhanced by the usual Hummel touches of flowers and birds. It will be listed as an Assigned Number until and if it is released for production and sale at some later time, when it will bear the current trademark. The German name is *Am Zaum* which means the same in English. A sample is in the Goebel archives. The sketch pictured here indicates the general appearance of the existing prototype.

324 At the Fence *(Assigned). Artist's concept.*

325 Helping Mother (Assigned Number)

Indicator	Size	Status	TMK-1	TMK-2	TMK-3	TMK-4	TMK-5	TMK-6
325	5″	A	—	—	—	—	—	?

When and if this little girl sewing at a table with a kitten is issued, it will be the second M.I. Hummel figurine to depict a cat in its design. It was taken from the same original drawing as was Hum. 133, Mother's Helper. This figurine was registered in the U.S. Copyright Office on July 18, 1956. Any prototypes that are discovered would probably carry a TMK-2 and be valued in the low four-digit figures. This remains an Assigned Number until Goebel releases it for production and distribution. The original English name was "Mother Said"; the German name, *Mutters grosse Stütze,* translates as "Mother's Big Support." Graphic H 201 has been published by Ars Edition.

325 Helping Mother *(Assigned). From H 201 courtesy Ars Edition.*

326 Being Punished (Assigned Number)

Indicator	Size	Status	TMK-1	TMK-2	TMK-3	TMK-4	TMK-5	TMK-6
326	5″	A	—	—	—	—	—	?

This piece will stand or hang as a plaque, if it is ever released for production. It was copyrighted in 1956 with U.S. Copyright GF15360 and with the same name. The German name *Jung im Karzer* translates as "Boy in Jail." When and if this piece is released for production and distributed by Goebel, it will probably carry the trademark current at the time. Any prototype found from 1956 with TMK-2 would be valued in the low four-digit figures. The original drawing owned by Ars Edition has been cataloged as H 200.

326 Being Punished *(Assigned). From H 200 courtesy Ars Edition.*

327 The Run-a-Way

Indicator	Size	Status	TMK-1	TMK-2	TMK-3	TMK-4	TMK-5	TMK-6
327	5½″	D,a	—	2,500	—	650	500	—
327	5½″	P,b	—	—	—	—	120	110

(a – 1955 copyright date. b – restyled with 1972 copyright date.)

This small fellow is also known as the "Happy Wanderer" from the German, *Der Frohe Wanderer.* When first registered in the U.S. Copyright Office in 1956, it was called "Roving Song." The piece is actually incised with the German copyright date of 1955. Hum. 327 was restyled in 1972. The original model has articles protruding from the basket; the newer one does not. The old version has a gray hat and jacket; the present one has a green hat and blue jacket. The present models can also be distinguished by the incised 1972 copyright date. An early prototype had TMK-2 stamped on it and would be valued in the low four-digit figures. Graphic H 218 was published by Ars Edition, owner of the original drawing.

327 The Run-a-Way, *copyright 1972, TMK-5.*

328   Carnival

Indicator	Size	Status	TMK-1	TMK-2	TMK-3	TMK-4	TMK-5	TMK-6
328	6″	D,a	—	2,500	—	—	—	—
328	6″	P,b	—	—	150	100	80	74
328	6″	D,c	—	—	—	125	—	—

(a – 1955 copyright. b – 1957 copyright, open pom-pom. c – 1957 copyright, closed pom-pom.)

The catalogs indicate that this was available for sale in the U.S. in the early 1960s at 5½″ high and was incised with a 1955 copyright date. A 1957 copyright was used from the 1960s on, and a variation in the pom-pom has been noted. A graphic was published by Ars Edition as H 259. The original drawing owned by Ars Edition shows another boy with a staff pictured on the right of Hum. 328.

328 Carnival, *copyright, 1957, TMK-4.*

329   Off to School (Assigned Number)

Indicator	Size	Status	TMK-1	TMK-2	TMK-3	TMK-4	TMK-5	TMK-6
329	?	A	—	—	—	—	—	—

The July 18, 1956, U.S. copyright refers to two figures called "On Way to School," 5″ high. It was referred to at one time as "Kindergarten Romance." The German name *Frisch gewagt* translates as "Freshly Dared Is Half Won." The boy appears similar to Hum. 82, School Boy, and the girl is carrying one of the ubiquitous German briefcases on her arm. If and when this is released, it will carry the trademark in use at the time. An early factory sample has been illustrated and if another is ever found, it should have TMK-2 and be valued in the mid four-digit figures. Graphic H 194 has been published by Ars Edition, who owns the original drawing.

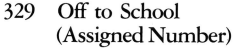

Frisch gewagt ist halb gewonnen!

329 Off to School *(Assigned). From H 194 courtesy Ars Edition.*

330   Baking Day (Assigned Number)

Indicator	Size	Status	TMK-1	TMK-2	TMK-3	TMK-4	TMK-5	TMK-6
330	?	A	—	—	—	—	—	?

This same name was used for the U.S. copyright which was registered on July 16, 1956. Apparently the figurine has also been referred to as "Kneading Dough." A picture of a factory sample has been published. If one of these becomes available for sale, it would be valued in the mid four-digit figures. This Assigned Number may or may not be approved for future production and, if so, it will probably be marked with the trademark in use at that time. The German name of *Die Bäckerin* translates as "The Baker Girl." The original drawing's location is undetermined at present and no gaphics have been issued.

330 Baking Day *(Assigned). Artist's concept.*

331 Crossroads

Indicator	Size	Status	TMK-1	TMK-2	TMK-3	TMK-4	TMK-5	TMK-6
331	6¾″	D,a	—	3,000	2,000	—	—	—
331	6¾″	P,b	—	—	—	400	195	175

(a – trombone with mouthpiece up. b – trombone with bell end up.)

The pieces are incised with copyright date 1955. When first issued, the boy with the slide trombone slung over his shoulder was carrying it with the mouthpiece at the top. This was altered so that TMK-4,5, and 6 show the boy with the trombone reversed, that is, with the bell of the horn pointing upward. Normally found with TMK-4 through TMK-6, an unverified report states that an example is known with TMK-3. The original drawing owned by Ars Edition has been published as graphic H 615.

331 Crossroads, *copyright 1955, TMK-5.*

332 Soldier Boy

Indicator	Size	Status	TMK-1	TMK-2	TMK-3	TMK-4	TMK-5	TMK-6
332	6″	D,a	—	2,500	—	—	—	—
332	6″	P,b	—	—	—	90	75	69
332	6″	D,c	—	—	—	135	—	—

(a – 1955 copyright prototype. b – 1957 copyright, blue button. c – 1957 copyright, red button.)

The first listing of this motif in early 1960 catalogs was Soldier Boy, 5½″ high. The U.S. copyright was registered in July of 1955 under the name of "Attention." A 1957 copyright is also found incised on some later models. Any prototype with TMK-2 would be valued in the low four-digit figures. The emblem on the soldier's cap was changed from a bright red for some 1957 models in TMK-4 to the present dark blue. The German name for this model is *Still gestanden!* for "At Attention." Graphic H 233 is published by Ars Edition, who owns the original drawing.

332 Soldier Boy, *copyright 1957, TMK-4.*

333 Blessed Event

Indicator	Size	Status	TMK-1	TMK-2	TMK-3	TMK-4	TMK-5	TMK-6
333	5½″	D,a	—	2,000?	500	—	—	—
333	5½″	P,b	—	—	350	250	155	140

(a – 1955 copyright. b – 1957 copyright.)

Introduced in the U.S. in 1964, the year of the New York World's Fair, the copyright goes back to 1955. This is found with TMK-3 through TMK-6. The question mark in the table for TMK-2 indicates the possibility that one of the early prototype samples will turn up in the marketplace. Graphic H 102 is published by Ars Edition, who owns the original drawing. The German name is *Das grosse Ereignis* for "The Big Event." In the 1960s, this was redesigned with the copyright year 1957 used.

333 Blessed Event, *copyright 1955, TMK-5.*

334 Homeward Bound

Indicator	Size	Status	TMK-1	TMK-2	TMK-3	TMK-4	TMK-5	TMK-6
334	5¼"	D,a	—	—	—	325	200	—
334	5¼"	D,b	—	—	—	300	180	—
334	5¼"	P,c	—	—	—	—	165	150

(a – 1955 copyright with post. b – 1956 copyright with post. c – 1975 copyright with no post.)

This motif did not appear in the U.S. catalogs until 1971 with the 1956 or the earlier 1955 copyright date incised on the bottom. An important restyling occurred in 1975. The simulated tree stump (under the goat for strength) was removed and Skrobek gave the new model the textured finish characteristic of his work. The possibility of an early sample with the TMK-2 reaching collectors' hands exists. The German name *Heimkehr vom Felde* stands for "Return Home from the Fields." Graphic H 314 is published by Ars Edition, owner of the original drawing.

334 Homeward Bound, *copyright 1956, TMK-5. New style.*

335 Lucky Boy (Assigned Number)

Indicator	Size	Status	TMK-1	TMK-2	TMK-3	TMK-4	TMK-5	TMK-6
335	5¾"	A	—	—	—	—	—	?

This was copyrighted in the U.S. on July 18, 1956, under this name. The German name *Der Glücksbub* means the same as the English one. Early samples for study, approval, and copyright purposes would have been marked with TMK-2. One of these is in the factory archives. This Assigned Number may or may not be released for production at some future date. When and if this happens, the pieces may be incised with a 1956 date, but with current trademark.

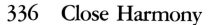

Viel Glück im neuen Jahr!

335 Lucky Boy *(Assigned). From H 339 courtesy Ars Edition.*

336 Close Harmony

Indicator	Size	Status	TMK-1	TMK-2	TMK-3	TMK-4	TMK-5	TMK-6
336	5½"	D,a	—	?	?	300	150	—
336	5½"	P,b	—	?	?	140	130	120

*(a – 1956 or 1957 copyright. b – 1955 copyright. **Note:** Possible prototypes for TMK 2 and 3 valued at 1,000+.)*

This piece was first cataloged in the early 1960s at 5½" high. Several different copyright dates (1955, 1956, and 1957) are incised on the bottom. The actual U.S. copyright, GP12644, was registered on July 17, 1956, under the name "Birthday Serenade," which was not used. This is still the name given in the German, *Geburtstagsständchen*. The diamond printed dress of the taller girl now appears to be diamond quilted. In the early models, the socks of each girl were even. Now the larger girl's right stocking is higher than the left, and the smaller girl's left stocking is higher than the right.

336 Close Harmony, *copyright 1956, trademark unknown.*

337 **Cinderella**, *eyes down, copyright 1975, TMK-5.*

337 Cinderella

Indicator	Size	Status	TMK-1	TMK-2	TMK-3	TMK-4	TMK-5	TMK-6
337	4½″	D,a	—	—	300	200	—	—
337	4½″	P,b	—	—	—	—	120	110

(a – eyes open, copyright incised 1958. b – eyes closed (down), copyright incised 1972.)

The figures are incised on the bottom with a 1958 date. Shortly after the introduction here in 1972, it was restyled and copyrighted on December 4, 1972. In the older 1958 version, the girl is looking up or almost straight ahead; whereas, in the present version the girl is looking down, textured, a la Skrobek. No postcards or other graphics have been found and the location of the original drawing is unknown. The German name, *Aschenputtel,* is the same as the English, "Cinderella."

338 **Birthday Cake**, *candleholder (Assigned). TMK-2, Miller Collection.*

338 Birthday Cake, Candleholder (Assigned Number)

Indicator	Size	Status	TMK-1	TMK-2	TMK-3	TMK-4	TMK-5	TMK-6
338	3¾″	A	—	4,000*	—	—	—	?

This was copyrighted in the U.S. on July 18, 1956. An early prototype of this motif with TMK-2 was exhibited by Robert Miller at the Eaton Festival in 1980. The German name, *Der Gerburtstagskuchen,* is the same as the English. This Assigned Number may be released for production and distribution at some future date. If it is released, it would be labeled with the trademark that is current at the time of issue. Ars Edition owns the original drawing and publishes graphic H 347 from it.

*Prototype in Miller Collection.

339 Behave (Assigned Number)

Indicator	Size	Status	TMK-1	TMK-2	TMK-3	TMK-4	TMK-5	TMK-6
339	5½″	A	—	—	—	—	—	?

This was called "Be Good" when copyrighted in the U.S. on July 17, 1956. When it will be released for production and sale is unknown, but it will probably carry a current transfer label at that time. At least one TMK-2 is in existence and has a value in the low four-digit range. The German name is *Wir gehen Spazieren,* which translates as "We're Going for a Walk."

339 **Behave** *(Assigned). From H 213 courtesy Ars Edition.*

340 Letter to Santa Claus

Indicator	Size	Status	TMK-1	TMK-2	TMK-3	TMK-4	TMK-5	TMK-6
340	7¼″	D,a	—	4,000	1,500	—	—	—
340	7¼″	P,b	—	—	?	300	145	130

(a – 1956 copyright, gray-green leggings and hat; TMK-2 is a prototype. b – 1957 copyright, red leggings and blue hat.)

This was registered as "Letter to Santa Claus" in the U.S. Copyright Office on August 15, 1957. It was first available in the U.S. in the very early 1970s with a TMK-4 mark. The most important differences apparent in the redesign are that present models have red snow pants and dark blue knitted caps with matching mufflers. They also have all the characteristics of Skrobek's modeling. A red stamp was also added to the new envelope. The revised version is found in TMK-4 through TMK-6; TMK-3 pieces have been reported. Graphic H 318 is published by Ars Edition, who owns the original drawing.

340 Letter to Santa Claus, *new style, TMK-4.*

341 Birthday Present (Assigned Number)

Indicator	Size	Status	TMK-1	TMK-2	TMK-3	TMK-4	TMK-5	TMK-6
341	5¼″	A	—	—	—	—	—	?

This 5¼″ figurine was registered in the U.S. Copyright Office on July 18, 1956. At least one sample exists. If someone is fortunate to locate another, it would be valued in the high four-digit figures. If this model is approved for production and sale, it would probably have the trademark current at the time of issue. The German name for this assigned design is *Das Geburtstagsgeschenk,"* having the same meaning as the English name. Ars Edition graphic H 347, from the original drawing, pictures this gift-bearer in the right foreground.

341 Birthday Present *(Assigned).* From H 347 courtesy Ars Edition.

342 Mischief Maker

Indicator	Size	Status	TMK-1	TMK-2	TMK-3	TMK-4	TMK-5	TMK-6
342	5″	D,a	—	—	—	300	200	—
342	5″	P,b	—	—	—	—	115	105

(a – 1958 copyright. b – 1960 copyright.)

It was first listed for sale at 5″ high and priced at $28.50 in the 1972 U.S. catalogs. It has been found identified with TMK-4 through TMK-6. It could be possible that earlier prototype pieces have a TMK-2 or 3. A verified prototype would be valued in the low four-digit figures. The German name for this figurine, *Der Störenfried,* is essentially the same as the English one. Graphic H 300 is published by Ars Edition, who owns the original drawing.

342 Mischief Maker, *copyright 1960, TMK-5.*

343 Christmas Song, *TMK-6, courtesy Goebel Collectors' Club.*

343 Christmas Song

Indicator	Size	Status	TMK-1	TMK-2	TMK-3	TMK-4	TMK-5	TMK-6
343	6½″	P	—	—	—	—	—	85

This was registered as "Angel with Stave," 6½″ high, in the U.S. Copyright Office on August 15, 1957. At least one factory sample is known and may well be a TMK-2, probably with an incised copyright date from the mid-1950s. Another authentic prototype should have a value in the mid four-digit figures. This was first issued in the fall of 1981 as one of six new figurines with TMK-6. The German name *Weihnachtslied* translates to the same in English. The original drawing by Sister Hummel is owned by Ars Edition, who has published graphic H 453 from it.

344 Feathered Friends, *copyright 1965, TMK-5.*

344 Feathered Friends

Indicator	Size	Status	TMK-1	TMK-2	TMK-3	TMK-4	TMK-5	TMK-6
344	4¾″	P	—	2,500	1,200	150	125	110

The German name *Schwanenteich* roughly translates as "Swan Pond." It was copyrighted in the U.S. on July 18, 1957, as "Feathered Friends." It has been listed in the U.S. catalogs since 1972 for $27.50 and incised with a 1956 copyright date on the base. An early sample reported by one collector has a 1956 copyright date and also a TMK-2. This piece, probably one of the approval samples or small test lots, was insured for $2,500. Graphic H 157 has been published by Ars Edition, who owns the original drawing.

345 A Fair Measure, *eyes down, copyright 1972, TMK-5.*

345 A Fair Measure

Indicator	Size	Status	TMK-1	TMK-2	TMK-3	TMK-4	TMK-5	TMK-6
345	5½″	D,a	—	2,000	1,000	500	—	—
345	5½″	P,b	—	—	—	—	120	110

(a – 1956 copyright, eyes open. b – 1972 copyright, eyes closed (looking down).)

When this was issued in Germany, it was and still is called *Der Kaufmann* or "The Merchant." It was registered using its English name in this country on August 15, 1957. It was not until 1972 that this piece was cataloged and sold in the U.S. for about $27. Soon after the introduction in the U.S., it was completely restyled in the "Skrobek manner." In the new 1972 version, the boy is looking down at the container on the scale instead of looking over the container. This model has been produced for sale in TMK-4 through TMK-6, except for the prototypes or approval samples. The original drawing by Sister Hummel has not been located and no graphics made from it have been found.

346   Smart Little Sister

Indicator	Size	Status	TMK-1	TMK-2	TMK-3	TMK-4	TMK-5	TMK-6
346	4¾"	P	—	—	300	120	100	90

This motif was actually registered on August 15, 1957, and appears in the U.S. catalogs about five years later incised with the year 1956 on the bottom. To date, no prototype examples or early samples marked with TMK-2 have been reported, even though such an unusual find is a possibility, and would be valued in the very high four-digit figures. The German name, *Das kluge Schwesterlein,* translates roughly as "The Clever Little Sister." The trefoil leaf design in the girl's apron is a welcome change from the usual polka dot on so many others. The original drawing is owned and published by Ars Edition as graphic H 193.

346 Smart Little Sister, *copyright 1956, TMK-5.*

347   Adventure Bound

Indicator	Size	Status	TMK-1	TMK-2	TMK-3	TMK-4	TMK-5	TMK-6
347	7½"	P	—	*	—	2,000	1,850	1,700

This sculpture in German is *Die sieben Schaben,* or "The Seven Swabians." It was copyrighted in the U.S. on October 4, 1957, as "Adventure Bound," with 1957 incised on the bottom of the figurine. This figurine, adapted from Sister Hummel's original drawing, was sculpted by Theodore R. Menzenbach, Goebel's master modeler at that time. Listed for the first time in U.S. catalogs in 1971, it is normally found marked only with TMK-4, 5, or 6. A few early samples or prototype pieces have been discovered which are valued in the mid four-digit range. Graphic H 214, from the original drawing, has been issued by Ars Edition.

*Prototype in Miller Collection.

347 Adventure Bound, *copyright 1957, TMK-5.*

348   Ring Around the Rosie

Indicator	Size	Status	TMK-1	TMK-2	TMK-3	TMK-4	TMK-5	TMK-6
348	6¾"	P	—	4,000?	2,000	1,600	1,400	1,250

This group of four girls first appeared in U.S. catalogs in the early 1960s, but carried the incised copyright date of 1957, the same year it was registered in the U.S. Copyright Office. There was no record of a later copyright found. In 1969, the suggested price for this piece was listed in U.S. catalogs at $100 marked with TMK-3. One early sample piece with TMK-2 has been reported and is valued in the low four-digit figures. The German name, *Ringelreihen,* translates the same as the English name. The original drawing by Sister Hummel is owned by Ars Edition from which graphic H 204 has been produced.

348 Ring Around the Rosie, *copyright 1957, TMK-5.*

349 The Florist (Assigned). From
H 113 courtesy Ars Edition.

349 The Florist (Assigned Number)

Indicator	Size	Status	TMK-1	TMK-2	TMK-3	TMK-4	TMK-5	TMK-6
349	7¼"	A	—	—	—	—	—	?

It was registered as "Boy with Flowers," 7¼" high, in the U.S. Copyright Office on April 21, 1961. A picture of a factory prototype has been published in Miller's HUMMEL *Authorized Supplement.* If a sample similar to that is found before the figure is released, it would probably be marked with TMK-3 and be valued in the mid four-digit figures. If this motif is approved for production and sale, it will probably have the same incised copyright, but with current trademark. The German name for this assigned model is *Der Blumenfreund,* which means "The Flower Friend (Lover)." Graphic H 113 has been published by Ars Edition, who owns the original drawing.

350 On Holiday

Indicator	Size	Status	TMK-1	TMK-2	TMK-3	TMK-4	TMK-5	TMK-6
350	4¼"	P	—	—	—	—	—	85

There is good news for collectors. This previously unissued figurine was first made available in the U.S. in the fall of 1981 for $85. Here is the background. On September 9, 1965, Goebel filed U.S. Copyright GF294 for Hum. 350, describing it as "Girl with Umbrella and Basket." Due to Robert Miller's efforts, a factory sample was located earlier of this motif, but it was never issued. The German name, *Zum Festtag,* would translate as "For the Holiday." Graphic H 356 has been published by Ars Edition, who owns the original drawing. The figurine is adapted from the girl on the right in the original drawing of three girls.

350 On Holiday, *issued 1981, TMK-6,
courtesy Goebel Collectors' Club.*

351 The Botanist

Indicator	Size	Status	TMK-1	TMK-2	TMK-3	TMK-4	TMK-5	TMK-6
351	4"	P	—	—	—	—	—	84

This adaptation was registered in the U.S. Copyright Office on May 30, 1972, with the unimaginative name "Girl Holding Flowers." It was released in the fall of 1982 with a new name, "The Botanist," with the current TMK-6 and the 1972 copyright date. If some collector is fortunate enough to acquire one of the prototypes; it would be valued in the mid four-digit figures. The German name assigned to this motif is *Enzian-Mädchen,* or "Girl with Gentian Flowers." Ars Edition owns the original drawing.

351 The Botanist, *issued 1982,
TMK-6, courtesy Goebel Collectors' Club.*

352 Sweet Greetings

Indicator	Size	Status	TMK-1	TMK-2	TMK-3	TMK-4	TMK-5	TMK-6
352	4¼"	P	—	—	—	—	—	85

This is another of several Assigned Numbers that was issued in the fall of 1981 for $85. First registered in the U.S. Copyright Office in 1965, it was called "Girl Standing by Fence." A prototype was later discovered in Goebel's archives of a girl holding a large red heart in her hands, 4¼" high. It is issued with TMK-6 only, except for the prototype, which is TMK-3 or 4. Another one of these, if found, would be valued in the mid four-digit figures. The German name, *Ein süsser Gruss,* means essentially the same as the English one. The original drawing published by Ars Edition, graphic H 356, shows three girls. The girl in the middle is the one adapted for the figurine.

352 **Sweet Greetings**, *issued 1981, TMK-6, courtesy Goebel Collectors' Club.*

353 Spring Dance

Indicator	Size	Status	TMK-1	TMK-2	TMK-3	TMK-4	TMK-5	TMK-6
353/0	5¼"	R	—	—	—	1,000	130	110
353/I	6¾"	D,t	—	—	—	320	275	250

(t – temporarily withdrawn, to be reinstated later.)

Some collectors will pay more for the small 5¼" size in TMK-4 than they will pay for the larger 6¾" size, because the small size was produced in very limited quantities until it was reissued in 1978. This piece was registered in the U.S. Copyright Office as "Spring Dance" on August 22, 1963. It was available for sale in the U.S. with the copyright year 1963 incised on the base, 7" high, for $33. The German name used at that time was *Frühlingstanz* and the model number incised on the base was 353/I. The large size, 353/I, was discontinued from the line early in 1982. The price on those produced may increase as a result. The design of this piece with two figures is suggestive of the four-figured Ring Around the Rosie, Hum. 348, and the 1980 Anniversary Plate, Hum. 281, by the same name. The present German name is *Sommertanz,* which translates as Summer Dance. No original drawing has been located, nor are there any graphics.

353/0 **Spring Dance**, *reissued in 1978, TMK-5.*

354 A Angel with Lantern, *Holy Water Font, (Assigned). Artist's concept.*

354A Angel with Lantern, Holy Water Font (Assigned Number)

Indicator	Size	Status	TMK-1	TMK-2	TMK-3	TMK-4	TMK-5	TMK-6
354A	5"	A	—	—	—	—	—	?

354 B Angel with Trumpet, *Holy Water Font, (Assigned). Artist's concept.*

354B Angel with Trumpet, Holy Water Font (Assigned Number)

Indicator	Size	Status	TMK-1	TMK-2	TMK-3	TMK-4	TMK-5	TMK-6
354B	5"	A	—	—	—	—	—	?

354C Angel with Bird and Cross, Holy Water Font (Assigned Number)

Indicator	Size	Status	TMK-1	TMK-2	TMK-3	TMK-4	TMK-5	TMK-6
354C	5"	A	—	—	—	—	—	?

In the first edition of *HUMMEL* by Eric Ehrmann, this number was listed as a Closed Number, one that was never used and never would be used. Further research by Robert Miller and the factory disclosed a trinity of font prototypes aptly described by the above names and assigned to this number until they are authorized for production or abandoned altogether. The abstract of the U.S. copyright may be incomplete as it shows only that Hum. 354 was registered as GP28607 on April 21,1961, with the name assigned as "Kneeling Angel with Horn." If a collector is of the opinion that she or he has discovered one or all three of these, the pieces should meet the triple test of being incised with the facsimile signature on the back, a model number of 354B also incised on the back at the top, and a motif that matches the name. It should also have an incised copyright date on the back of about 1961 and either a TMK-3 or TMK-4 company mark. Any one example found fulfilling these requirements would be valued from the high hundreds to a thousand dollars. Refer to Hum. 357, 358, and 359 for somewhat similar figurines.

354 C Angel with Bird and Cross, *Holy Water Font, (Assigned). Artist's concept.*

355 Autumn Harvest

Indicator	Size	Status	TMK-1	TMK-2	TMK-3	TMK-4	TMK-5	TMK-6
355	4¾"	P	—	—	—	200	93	84

The figurine is known in German as *Herbstsegen* or "Fall Blessings." Registration of this design is dated April 9, 1964, in the U.S. Copyright Office, and production pieces are incised to this day with that date on the bottom. Presently the hair is more accentuated by a "wiped," two-tone finish. A piece with TMK-3 would be quite unusual. This appears to have been adapted from an original drawing owned by Ars Edition which has a lamb and a pennant topped by a cross in the girl's basket, instead of the fruit. See graphic H 380 published by Ars Edition for an exact replica of the original Sister Hummel drawing.

355 **Autumn Harvest,** *copyright 1964, TMK-5.*

356 Gay Adventure

Indicator	Size	Status	TMK-1	TMK-2	TMK-3	TMK-4	TMK-5	TMK-6
356	5"	P	—	—	—	150	80	70

First cataloged in the U.S. in 1972 along with about twenty other new models, this was copyrighted only the year before in the U.S. on December 3, and incised 1971. It is found with TMK-4, 5, and 6. The German name *Frohes Wandern* translates as "Happy Wandering." It was used as the illustration for September in the 1978 calendar. The original drawing is owned by Ars Edition and a graphic from it is produced as H 494.

Mass from New Merck 10/82

1971 - "Re 81   *52 for Joyful adventure*

356 **Gay Adventure,** *copyright 1971, TMK-5.*

357 Guiding Angel

Indicator	Size	Status	TMK-1	TMK-2	TMK-3	TMK-4	TMK-5	TMK-6
357	2¾"	P	—	—	—	60	45	40

This angel was copyrighted as a figurine, GP28613, April 21, 1961, and cataloged in the U.S. for the first time in 1972. At that time it was listed for $11. The incised copyright date on the bottom of each piece is 1960. This may have been visualized as one of a set. One U.S. catalog has merely listed 357, 358, and 359 as "Angels Assorted," 2¾" high. No record has been found of graphics produced or of the original drawing by Sister Hummel. The German name *Kniender Engel mit Laterne* is very descriptive of this piece and translates as "Kneeling Angel with Lantern."

357 **Guiding Angel,** *copyright 1960, TMK-5.*

358 Shining Light, *TMK-5.*

358 Shining Light

Indicator	Size	Status	TMK-1	TMK-2	TMK-3	TMK-4	TMK-5	TMK-6
358	2¾"	P	—	—	—	60	45	40

This piece apparently was thought of as one of a set and was so listed in some catalogs. Therefore, the historical information for this narrative is identical to Hum. 357. If a protoyte or early sample were found, it might well carry the earlier TMK-3 identification and therefore be a premium piece valued at several hundred dollars. The German name *Kniender Engel mit Kerze* is descriptive of the figure and translates as "Kneeling Angel with Candle." No record of the original painting or graphics has been found to date.

359 Tuneful Angel, *TMK-5.*

359 Tuneful Angel

Indicator	Size	Status	TMK-1	TMK-2	TMK-3	TMK-4	TMK-5	TMK-6
359	2¾"	P	—	—	—	60	45	40

This figurine is the third of the set. It also was listed in some catalogs, together with the two preceding figurines, as "Angels Three, Assorted." Most of the historical information on this piece is identical to Hum. 358, which should be referred to for more information. The German name, *Kniender Engel mit Trompete,* translates as "Kneeling Angel with Trumpet."

360/A Boy and Girl, *Wall Vase, reissue, c. 1958, TMK-5.*

360/A Boy and Girl, Wall Vase

Indicator	Size	Status	TMK-1	TMK-2	TMK-3	TMK-4	TMK-5	TMK-6
360/A	6"	R	—	—	450	—	66	50

Once considered rare, in 1979 it was listed in the U.S. catalogs at $50 and promptly escalated about 300 percent in price in the secondary market, which was about half the price of rare TMK-3 examples. These premiums may be highly dependent on the future production of the Goebel Company. This design as a wall vase was registered in the U.S. Copyright Office on December 10, 1958. All production examples since that time have been incised with the 1958 copyright date. This would indicate that if an example were ever found with a TMK-2, it originally might have been a prototype piece or sample used for copyright or other purposes. Location of the original drawing is undetermined.

360/B   Boy, Wall Vase

Indicator	Size	Status	TMK-1	TMK-2	TMK-3	TMK-4	TMK-5	TMK-6
360/B	6″	R	—	—	400	—	66	60

As mentioned under 360/A, to which one should refer for complete detail, this motif of the boy only was copyrighted at the same time, December 10, 1958. The relatively few examples that have been found all carry the TMK-3. This was reintroduced in 1978-1979 at the same price of $50 and did a similar upward spiral in the secondary market, where prices may or may not remain. No original drawing has been found that would show what 360/A and its two counterparts were derived from. The German name for this piece and the two others is the same as the English.

360/B Boy, *Wall Vase, reissue, copyright 1958, TMK-5.*

360/C   Girl, Wall Vase

Indicator	Size	Status	TMK-1	TMK-2	TMK-3	TMK-4	TMK-5	TMK-6
360/C	6″	R	—	—	400	—	66	60

The story of the last of the three related vases, 6″ high, is fully covered in the information about Hum. 360/A and Hum. 360/B. Their careers from the copyright date of December 10, 1958, show a remarkable parallel as to events, trademarks, scarcity, and suggested retail price. They do differ in valuations in the secondary market. As might be expected, the wall vase with both the boy and the girl in the motif commands a higher price than either of the other two with single figures.

360/C Girl, *Wall Vase, reissue, copyright 1958, TMK-5. Courtesy W. Goebel Co.*

361   Favorite Pet

Indicator	Size	Status	TMK-1	TMK-2	TMK-3	TMK-4	TMK-5	TMK-6
361	4¼″	P	—	—	350	120	105	95

This three-dimensional adaptation was copyrighted in the U.S. on April 21, 1961, under the above name. The copyright that is incised on the production pieces is 1960. It was listed in the U.S. catalogs in 1964. Since then, catalogs show a variety of sizes from present 4¼″ to 5″ high. Any premium for the larger pieces is reflected above for the earlier trademarks. As with so many others, the German name *Ostergruss* or "Easter Greeting" is unrelated to the name used in the U.S., "Favorite Pet." The original drawing by Sister Hummel is owned by Ars Edition from which a graphic was published as H 375.

361 Favorite Pet, *copyright 1960, TMK-5.*

362 I Forgot (Assigned Number)

Indicator	Size	Status	TMK-1	TMK-2	TMK-3	TMK-4	TMK-5	TMK-6
362	5½"	A	—	—	—	—	—	?

When the copyright was issued in the U.S. on April 21, 1961, it was merely described as "Girl with Basket and Doll." Several years ago this number was listed as an Open Number. Due to more research by Robert Miller and Goebel, a prototype was found in the company archives. If and when this piece is issued, it will probably be incised with a 1960 or 1961 copyright date and will carry the trademark currently in use at that time. The original by Sister Hummel is owned by Ars Edition from which graphic H 341 was made. The German name, *Ich hab's vergessen,* means "I Have Forgotten."

362 **I Forgot** *(Assigned). From H 341 courtesy Ars Edition.*

363 Big Housecleaning

Indicator	Size	Status	TMK-1	TMK-2	TMK-3	TMK-4	TMK-5	TMK-6
363	4"	P	—	—	—	300	125	110

This diligent girl figurine was registered in the U.S. on April 21, 1961. It was cataloged for the first time in the U.S. in 1972 at 4" high. At that time the retail price was $28.50 with TMK-4 insignia and incised with a 1960 copyright year. If a collector is fortunate enough to obtain a verified early sample or prototype, it would be valued in the low four-digit figures. The German name, *Grossreinemachen,* means "Big Cleaning" in English. The original drawing by Sister Hummel is unlocated, as are any graphics.

363 **Big Housecleaning,** *copyright 1960, TMK-5.*

364 Supreme Protection, Madonna (Assigned Number)

Indicator	Size	Status	TMK-1	TMK-2	TMK-3	TMK-4	TMK-5	TMK-6
364	8¾"	A	—	—	—	—	—	?

This number was listed a few years ago as an Open Number that had never been assigned to any design. The author found that 364 had been copyrighted in the U.S. on April 9, 1964, as GF208, "Madonna and Child." Hum. 364 has a mantle with six-pointed stars versus the star formed of five dots in Hum. 10. The under robe is in a rich gold with intricate embossings. She wears a jeweled crown topped with a cross. The Child also wears a jeweled crown and ornate robe. Any prototype or early sample discovered would probably have either a TMK-3 or TMK-4 and would be valued in the mid four-digit figures. The German name, *Schutzmantel-Madonna,* means "Protected Cloak Madonna." Verlag Emil Fink has published postcard 219 from it.

364 **Supreme Protection,** *Madonna (Assigned). From #219, courtesy Emil Fink.*

365 Littlest Angel (Assigned Number)

Indicator	Size	Status	TMK-1	TMK-2	TMK-3	TMK-4	TMK-5	TMK-6
365	2½″	A	—	—	—	—	—	?

This is another unissued prototype discovered in Goebel's archives. This sculpture of a 2½″ seated figure with close-cropped hair resembles a life study of a small baby with wings that look like the gossamer wings of a bee. The German name, *'s Hummele,* ("It's a Bumblebee") may indicate her intention to portray a human child as having "busy bee" characteristics. The English name "Littlest Angel" is bland and rather humorless compared to the German name. This was copyrighted in the U.S. on April 9, 1964, and any sample made at that time would likely be incised with TMK-3 or TMK-4. Ars Edition, owner of the original drawing, uses it to publish graphic H 106.

365 Littlest Angel *(Assigned). From H 106 courtesy Ars Edition.*

366 Flying Angel

Indicator	Size	Status	TMK-1	TMK-2	TMK-3	TMK-4	TMK-5	TMK-6
366	3½″	P,a	—	—	—	70	59	53
366	3½″	P,b	—	—	—	25	21	19

(a – color. b – white glaze.)

A 1972 addition to the small Nativity Set, Hum. 214, was previously copyrighted on April 6, 1964, under the same name, and production pieces are incised with that copyright year. It is an angel designed to be hung at the top of the stable, thereby creating an impression of a flying angel, or as an ornament to hang on the Christmas tree. The original drawing of this motif is owned by Ars Edition, who publishes graphic H 480.

366 Flying Angel, *copyright 1964, TMK-5.*

367 Busy Student

Indicator	Size	Status	TMK-1	TMK-2	TMK-3	TMK-4	TMK-5	TMK-6
367	4½″	P	—	—	200	90	76	69

This studious girl was not copyrighted in the U.S. until October 14, 1967, even though 1963 is the copyright year incised on the base. Notice the similarity between this motif and the girl in Smart Little Sister, Hum. 346. This piece was first sold in this country in 1964 and is found in TMK-3 through TMK-6 with the incised copyright year of 1963. The German name *Musterschülerin* translates as "Model Pupil." This was extracted from an original drawing used for Smart Little Sister, Hum. 346, as can be seen in graphic H 193 published by Ars Edition.

367 Busy Student, *copyright 1963, TMK-5.*

368 Lute Song (Assigned Number)

Indicator	Size	Status	TMK-1	TMK-2	TMK-3	TMK-4	TMK-5	TMK-6
368	5"	A	—	—	—	—	—	?

When this was first registered in the U.S. Copyright Office on October 14, 1967, it was described as "Small Girl with Banjo, 5" high." Later, Robert Miller and the Goebel Company found a prototype in the company archives which verified this. Lute Song appears to be identical to one of the Close Harmony pair, Hum. 336, except for coloring and some details. The German name, *Lautenspiel,* translates as "Lute Play." When and if this is issued in the future, it will probably be incised with the German copyright and the trademark current at that time. Any prototype found before then would have a value in the mid four-digit figures.

368 Lute Song *(Assigned). Artist's concept.*

369 Follow the Leader

Indicator	Size	Status	TMK-1	TMK-2	TMK-3	TMK-4	TMK-5	TMK-6
369	7"	P	—	—	—	700	475	430

This very popular figurine was cataloged for sale in the U.S. in 1972. The year 1964 is incised on the base. If any early prototype or copyright sample reached the market and was fully authenticated, it would be valued in the low four-digit figures and might have the earlier TMK-3. The original drawing by Sister Hummel, from which this three-dimensional adaptation was derived, is owned by Ars Edition. Graphic H 351 has been published from the original. The German name, *Mach mit,* means "Follow the Leader."

369 Follow the Leader, *copyright 1964, TMK-5.*

370 Companions (Assigned Number)

Indicator	Size	Status	TMK-1	TMK-2	TMK-3	TMK-4	TMK-5	TMK-6
370	4½"	A	—	—	—	—	—	?

A few years ago nothing was believed to have been designed with this number. The U.S. Copyright Office records indicated otherwise. On September 9, 1965, registration number GF290 issued to Goebel described Hum. 370 as "Two Boys, One with Basket." Later, Robert Miller and the Goebel Company found this to be the case by locating a prototype with this number, 4½" high, in the company archives. Records indicated that this had been modeled by Gerhard Skrobek in 1964. If another sample should appear, it would be valued in the low four-digit figures. Verlag Emil Fink owns the original and has published postcard 207 and print 112.

370 Companions *(Assigned). From #207, courtesy Emil Fink.*

371 Daddy's Girls
(Assigned Number)

Indicator	Size	Status	TMK-1	TMK-2	TMK-3	TMK-4	TMK-5	TMK-6
371	4½"	A	—	—	—	—	—	?

The history of this unissued but potential figurine parallels almost exactly that of the preceding item, Hum. 370, Companions, as it is believed to have been intended as one of two figurines that would make an interesting pair. In fact, in German, each one has a similar name, *Gratulanten-Muttertag,* or "Congratulants, Mother's Day," for Hum. 370 and, *Gratulanten-Vatertag,* or "Congratulants, Father's Day," for Hum. 371.

371 Daddy's Girl's *(Assigned). From #208, courtesy Emil Fink.*

372 Blessed Mother, Madonna
(Assigned Number)

Indicator	Size	Status	TMK-1	TMK-2	TMK-3	TMK-4	TMK-5	TMK-6
372	10¼"	A	—	—	—	—	—	?

Originally in 1976 this was listed as a number that had never been assigned or used, but might be used in the future. Shortly thereafter, a search of the U.S. copyright records indicated that Hum. 372 was registered on September 9, 1965, as a figurine described as "Standing Madonna with Child," 10½" high. A later search of Goebel Company archives confirmed this to be the case, and a prototype of the figurine was found with the record that it had been done by the present master modeler, Gerhard Skrobek. If another sample of this figure is found prior to issue, it will no doubt have a TMK-3 or TMK-4 as the company identification, and be valued between one and two thousand dollars. Ars Edition owns the original and has used it to publish graphic H 532.

372 Blessed Mother *(Assigned). From H 532 courtesy Ars Edition.*

373 Just Fishing
(Assigned Number)

Indicator	Size	Status	TMK-1	TMK-2	TMK-3	TMK-4	TMK-5	TMK-6
373	4½"	A	—	—	—	—	—	?

In an early book on Hummel figurines published in 1976, this number was listed as a number that had not been used or assigned to any model, but might be used in the future. Later that same year, a record in variance with this statement was found in the U.S. Copyright Office. A copyright was registered by Goebel on September 9, 1965, as GF292 and described as Hum. 373, "Boy Fishing, 4½" high. Research since then uncovered an actual sample model in the Goebel Company archives. Ars Edition published graphic H 237 from the original drawing. In German the name is *Der Fischer,* meaning "The Fisherman." When and if this design is released for public sale, it probably will be incised with either a 1964 or 1965 copyright date on the base and the trademark then in use. If another sample of this motif should be found before then, it may have either TMK-3 or TMK-4 on the base and be valued in the low four-digit figures.

373 Just Fishing *(Assigned). From H 237 courtesy Ars Edition.*

374 Lost Stocking

Indicator	Size	Status	TMK-1	TMK-2	TMK-3	TMK-4	TMK-5	TMK-6
374	4½"	P	—	—	—	200	66	60

Not only has this boy lost his stocking, but his left shoe is also off. This piece was one of five new designs registered in the U.S. Copyright Office on September 9, 1965. It was listed by the above name as GR293, 4½" high. Examples are incised 1965. It was first found in a 1972 catalog. The current price is about three times what it was in 1972. It has been reported with TMK-4 through TMK-6. To date, there have been no significant variations in size, color, or design reported, although there may have been some. The original drawing of this motif by Sister Hummel has not been located to date and neither have the graphics, if there are any. The German name *Hab mein Strumpf verloren* translates as "Lost My Stocking."

374 Lost Stocking, *copyright 1965, TMK-5.*

375 Morning Stroll (Assigned Number)

Indicator	Size	Status	TMK-1	TMK-2	TMK-3	TMK-4	TMK-5	TMK-6
375	4¼"	A	—	—	—	—	—	?

For some time, published information indicated that this number had not been used by the Goebel Company for a specific figurine, but might be used at some later date. Further investigation revealed that this was not the case, as a copyright had been registered in the U.S. Copyright Office on September 9, 1965. The piece was described as Hum. 375, "Girl with doll carriage and dog," GF287. Still later, an actual example was found in the Goebel archives. The German name for this is *Ausfahrt* which means "Stroll." Any authentic prototype would be valued in the low four-digit range. Graphic H 215 has been published from the original drawing by Ars Edition.

375 Morning Stroll *(Assigned). From H 215 courtesy Ars Edition.*

376 Little Nurse

Indicator	Size	Status	TMK-1	TMK-2	TMK-3	TMK-4	TMK-5	TMK-6
376	4"	P	—	—	—	—	—	95

On page 45 of a small book published by Ars Edition, entitled *Sonntagsbüchlein,* there is a picture of a drawing by Sister Hummel showing a small angel advising a young boy about his bandaged finger. A copyright found registered on May 30, 1972, as Hum. 375, "A little girl dressed as a nurse," seemed to have little in common with the picture in the book. Research by Robert Miller and the Goebel Company found a prototype with the same little boy sitting on the stool, but instead of an angel, the figure is a girl dressed in a gray nurse's uniform. This figurine was first issued in the fall of 1982.

376 Little Nurse, *issued 1982, TMK-6, courtesy Goebel Collectors' Club.*

377 Bashful

Indicator	Size	Status	TMK-1	TMK-2	TMK-3	TMK-4	TMK-5	TMK-6
377	4¾"	P	—	—	—	225	80	74

The bottom of this figurine is incised with a 1966 copyright date. It was not copyrighted in this country until December of 1971. It was first listed for sale in distributors' catalogs for 1972. This was one of the group of twenty-four new figurines introduced for the first time in the U.S. in 1972. This little girl with the basket behind her has the German name *Vergissmeinnicht* meaning "Forget Me Not." If an early sample of the prototype became available, which is very unlikely, it might be marked with the earlier TMK-3. The original drawing, owned by Ars Edition, was used to publish print H 350 as an exact duplicate.

377 **Bashful**, *copyright 1966, TMK-5.*

378 Easter Greetings

Indicator	Size	Status	TMK-1	TMK-2	TMK-3	TMK-4	TMK-5	TMK-6
378	5¼"	P	—	—	—	300	92	84

This young boy was first registered in this country on December 3, 1971, under the same name. The German name *Ostergruss* appears to be identical to the English one. The figurine is incised with the 1971 copyright date on the underside of the base. In 1972, this motif first appeared for sale in the U.S. Essentially, there have been no important deviations reported in the 5¼" height, the colors, or design. It is found with TMK-4, 5, or 6. A picture of this figurine was used for the month of March in the 1980 calendar. The original drawing is owned by Ars Edition, who has published graphic H 379 as an exact replica of the original.

378 Easter Greetings, *TMK-5.*

379 Don't Be Shy
(Assigned Number)

Indicator	Size	Status	TMK-1	TMK-2	TMK-3	TMK-4	TMK-5	TMK-6
379	4½"	A	—	—	—	—	—	?

This is another number that was thought at first not to have been assigned to any motif, but reserved for use at some future date. The copyright record found in 1976 indicated differently, as it listed this number already registered by Goebel in the U.S. as GF833 on May 30, 1972, and described it as "Little girl feeding a bird on a fence." Robert Miller states that this was assigned as early as 1966. It will probably be incised with a copyright date 1966 and be identified by the trademark being used by Goebel at release time. Any other early samples that might surface from some unexpected source would be valued in the low to mid four-digit figure range. The original drawing of this subject by Sister Hummel was published by Verlag Emil Fink as postcard 698. The German name *Da, nimm's doch* means "Here, Take It."

379 **Don't Be Shy** *(Assigned). From #698, courtesy Emil Fink.*

380 Daisies Don't Tell

Indicator	Size	Status	TMK-1	TMK-2	TMK-3	TMK-4	TMK-5	TMK-6
380	4½″	D	—	—	—	—	—	80

This exclusive design for fifth-year members of the Goebel Collectors' Club was designed by Gerhard Skrobek in 1966 from an original drawing by Sister Hummel, now owned and published by Ars Edition as H 127. It was registered in the U.S. Copyright Office in 1972. The German name, *Er liebt mich*, translates as "He Loves Me." The purchase of this figurine will be limited to new or renewal memberships in the Goebel Collectors' Club starting in June 1981, and ending the last of May 1982. It can only be obtained by submitting a redemption card, received with the membership card, to an authorized Hummel dealer. It may take the dealer several weeks to redeem your card for the figurine which is priced at $80.

380 Daisies Don't Tell, *TMK-6, courtesy Goebel Collectors' Club.*

381 Flower Vendor

Indicator	Size	Status	TMK-1	TMK-2	TMK-3	TMK-4	TMK-5	TMK-6
381	5¼″	P	—	—	—	200	105	95

This boy was copyrighted in the U.S. on December 3, 1971, which is the same year that is incised on the underneath side of the base. The following year, 1972, it was cataloged for sale in this country for $24. This is found marked with either TMK-4, 5, or 6 and to date no major variations in color or design have been reported. The original drawing is owned by Ars Edition, who published it as graphic H 208. The German name *Zum Blumenmarkt* translates as "To the Flower Market."

381 Flower Vendor, *copyright 1971. TMK-5.*

382 Visiting an Invalid

Indicator	Size	Status	TMK-1	TMK-2	TMK-3	TMK-4	TMK-5	TMK-6
382	5″	P	—	—	—	275	100	90

This was copyrighted in the U.S. on December 3, 1971. The same year is incised on the underneath side of the base. The very next year, it was offered for sale in a 1972 distributor's catalog. The German name for this model is *Krankenbesuch* and translates as "Visit to a Patient." It is identified with either TMK-4, 5, or 6. So far there have been no important changes in size, color, or design reported. Later, something interesting may be discovered. The original drawing is owned by Verlag Emil Fink, from which a graphic was published as postcard 810.

382 Visiting an Invalid, *copyright 1971, TMK-5.*

383 Going Home (Assigned Number)

Indicator	Size	Status	TMK-1	TMK-2	TMK-3	TMK-4	TMK-5	TMK-6
383	4¼"	A	—	—	—	—	—	?

Several years ago, this was one of a series of numbers termed "Open Numbers" with no design assigned. Research has disclosed that a copyright had been filed in the U.S., and a prototype model and records were located at the factory. It was designed in 1966 by Gerhard Skrobek. The German name *Wanderfreunde* means "Wandering Friends." When and if this motif is for sale, it will probably be incised with the 1966 copyright date and be identified with the trademark in use by the company at release time. Any other sample which might show up of this pair would be valued in the mid four-digit figures. Ars Edition owns the original drawing and has published it as an exact replica, graphic H 217.

383 Going Home *(Assigned). From H 217 courtesy Ars Edition.*

384 Easter Time

Indicator	Size	Status	TMK-1	TMK-2	TMK-3	TMK-4	TMK-5	TMK-6
384	4"	P	—	—	—	200	132	120

The German name for this pair of girls with two rabbits is *Osterfreunde,* which means "Easter Playmates," suggesting the possibility that this might have been intended as a companion figurine to the boy with three rabbits called Playmates, Hum. 58. However, Easter Time was used when the copyright was registered in the U.S. on December 3, 1971. The same year is found incised on the underside of the base. The U.S. catalogs for 1972 list this motif for the first time. The original drawing by Sister Hummel, from which this was adapted, is owned by Verlag Emil Fink, who has published it as postcard 652.

384 Easter Time, *TMK-5.*

385 Chicken-Licken

Indicator	Size	Status	TMK-1	TMK-2	TMK-3	TMK-4	TMK-5	TMK-6
385	4¾"	P	—	—	—	200	132	120

This figurine is also called "Chicken Liesl" which is the translation of the German, *Kükenliesl.* However, Chicken-Licken was the name under which the copyright was registered in the U.S. on December 3, 1971, and incised on the underside of the base. To date, there has been no indication that there are any variations of the motif in color, size, or design which would be worth a premium over regular models. It appears to have been made by Gerhard Skrobek. The first U.S. catalog to list this piece for sale is the 1972 issue which listed it at $28.50. The original drawing is owned by Ars Edition who published graphic H 376.

385 Chicken-Licken, *TMK-5.*

386   On Secret Path

Indicator	Size	Status	TMK-1	TMK-2	TMK-3	TMK-4	TMK-5	TMK-6
386	5¼″	P	—	—	—	250	125	110

The inspiration for Sister Hummel's original drawing was her brother, Adolf. One night he was especially weary after working a part-time job, and he fell asleep in a neighbor's haystack on the way home, only to awake around midnight. He was pictured by his sister hurrying home with hay trailing from under his arms. The crickets were probably added for luck, to forestall or to ease the spanking he was sure to get for such a tardy arrival. It was registered in the U.S. Copyright Office in 1971. The base is incised with that date. The following year, 1972, it was listed in the U.S. catalogs. The German name, *Auf heimlichen Wegen*, translates the same in English. Verlag Emil Fink published it as postcard 697.

386 On Secret Path, *TMK-5*.

387   Valentine Gift

Indicator	Size	Status	TMK-1	TMK-2	TMK-3	TMK-4	TMK-5	TMK-6
387	5¼″	D,a	—	—	—	1,000	—	—
387	5¼″	D,b	—	—	—	—	225	—

(a – 1968 copyright. b – 1972 copyright.)

This figurine is a very special Limited Edition. One was produced for each first-year member of the Goebel Collectors' Club. Each first-year member was issued a redemption card with his or her membership card. The card could be redeemed for this figurine by presenting it to any authorized M. I. Hummel dealer together with $45. So many non-members want this that it has been resold for five times the issue price. The design was registered in the U.S. on May 30, 1972. The inscription says in German, *i hab di gern*, which translates as "I love you very much." The same year, 1972, is incised on the underside of the base. The blue transfer label reads "Exclusive Special Edition No. 1 for Members of the Goebel Collectors' Club. Graphic H 336 is published by Ars Edition, who owns the original drawing.

387 Valentine Gift, *Limited Edition, TMK-5*.

388   Little Band, Candleholder

Indicator	Size	Status	TMK-1	TMK-2	TMK-3	TMK-4	TMK-5	TMK-6
388	3″	P	—	—	—	160	140	125

On October 16, 1968, a series of five copyrights was issued in the U.S. using three different seated figurines, individually or collectively, as Hum. 388 through 392. This particular piece shows the three figures seated on a 4¾″ diameter round base with a candle socket in the center. The 1968 copyright date is incised on the underside of the base. It is only found with TMK-4, 5, or 6, and the date it was first offered for sale is not definite in the available catalogs. By 1973 the whole series from Hum. 388 through Hum. 392 was cataloged for sale.

388 Little Band, *Candleholder, TMK-5*.

388/M Little Band, Music Box-Candleholder

Indicator	Size	Status	TMK-1	TMK-2	TMK-3	TMK-4	TMK-5	TMK-6
388/M	3″	P	—	—	—	245	215	195

This combination consists of Hum. 388 Candleholder mounted as a cover on a wooden music box purchased from another source. Several tunes have reportedly been issued. The 1968 copyright date is incised on the base of this article. The three figures, either individually or collectively, have not been identified in Sister Hummel's drawings, nor in the graphics published from them.

388/M Little Band, *Music Box, Candleholder, TMK-5. Dous Collection.*

389 Girl with Sheet Music

Indicator	Size	Status	TMK-1	TMK-2	TMK-3	TMK-4	TMK-5	TMK-6
389	2½″	P	—	—	—	45	35	30

This is the 2½″ figure that is one of the three pieces mounted on the two previous Hummel numbers. In some catalogs, this piece, Hum. 390, and Hum. 391 are listed as "Children Trio" and sold by the set or individually. To clarify the names, these three pieces as a set are listed in the Alphabetical Index as Children Trio (B), to distinguish this one from another three-piece set called Children Trio (A), Hum. 239 A, Hum. 239 B, and Hum. 239 C. The German name *Mädchen mit Notenblatt* is the same as the English name.

389 Girl with Sheet Music, *foil label, TMK-5.*

390 Boy with Accordion

Indicator	Size	Status	TMK-1	TMK-2	TMK-3	TMK-4	TMK-5	TMK-6
390	2½″	P	—	—	—	45	35	30

This second individual piece of the trio may be sold as part of Children Trio (B) or individually. The incised copyright date is 1968. The German name, *Junge mit Bandoneon,* is the same as the English one. Due to the small size of figures such as these, the marking may be indistinct or in some cases the form or kind may be altered to suit conditions.

390 Boy with Accordion, *foil label, TMK-5.*

391 Girl with Trumpet

Indicator	Size	Status	TMK-1	TMK-2	TMK-3	TMK-4	TMK-5	TMK-6
391	2½″	P	—	—	—	45	35	30

The third seated figure is identified with an incised 1968 date. With this small trio, the M. I. Hummel signature is small and sometimes faint due to uneven surfaces to which it is applied. These have been identified with an aluminum foil label imprinted with the trademark, which is necessary because there is insufficient room on the base.

391 Girl with Trumpet, *foil label, TMK-5.*

392   Little Band

Indicator	Size	Status	TMK-1	TMK-2	TMK-3	TMK-4	TMK-5	TMK-6
392	3″	P	—	—	—	155	135	125

Once again the three figures in this series of arrangements are mounted on a common circular base. The only difference between this one and the first one, Hum. 388, is there is no candle socket in Hum. 392. Therefore, it is classed as a figurine and not a candleholder. Both versions are cataloged under their respective categories and sell for the same price. This is also incised 1968 on the base, representing the copyright year, and is found in TMK-4, 5, or 6. No important variations in style or color have been reported to date.

392 Little Band, *on base, TMK-5.*

392/M   Little Band, Music Box

Indicator	Size	Status	TMK-1	TMK-2	TMK-3	TMK-4	TMK-5	TMK-6
392/M	3″	P	—	—	—	245	215	195

The difference between this box and Hum. 338/M is the absence of a candle socket in this model. The other statements that apply to Hum. 338/M are applicable here. The German name *Kindergruppe auf Musikwerk* translates as "Group of Children on Music Box." The original drawings of these children have not been located and no graphics by either Ars Edition or Verlag Emil Fink have been found.

392/M Little Band, *Music Box, copyright 1964, TMK-4.*

393   Dove, Holy Water Font (Assigned Number)

Indicator	Size	Status	TMK-1	TMK-2	TMK-3	TMK-4	TMK-5	TMK-6
393	4¼″	A	—	—	—	—	—	?

This was formerly thought to have been an Open Number, one that had not been used for a design. A search of the company archives in the last few years revealed that this number had been assigned to a holy water font designed by Gerhard Skrobek in 1968. No record was found of the registration of the design in the U.S. A prototype of this piece is pictured in Robert Miller's *HUMMEL, Authorized Supplement*. The dove is the religious representation of the Holy Spirit and the words on the banner are *Komm Heiliger Geist* for "Come Holy Ghost." The German title, *Weihkessel, Taube,* is essentially the same as the English name. The original drawing is owned by Ars Edition.

393 Dove, *Holy Water Font (Assigned). From H 387 courtesy Ars Edition.*

394 Timid Little Sister

Indicator	Size	Status	TMK-1	TMK-2	TMK-3	TMK-4	TMK-5	TMK-6
394	6½"	P	—	—	—	—	—	190

This is one of the six new figurines first offered in the U.S. in the fall of 1981, showing the boy and girl looking intently at something on the ground. The U.S. copyright issued in 1972 describes it as "A little boy and girl looking at a frog." A few years later a prototype was located in the factory archives and indicated it had been adapted from the original drawing with the addition of a frog by Gerhard Skrobek. The German name, *Das angstliche Schwesterlein,* translates essentially the same as Hum. 394, omitting any reference to the boy. This motif was published by Emil Fink as postcard 206 which does not include the frog.

394 Timid Little Sister, *issued 1981, TMK-6, courtesy Goebel Collectors' Club.*

395 Shepherd Boy (Assigned Number)

Indicator	Size	Status	TMK-1	TMK-2	TMK-3	TMK-4	TMK-5	TMK-6
395	6"	A	—	—	—	—	—	?

An early book on M. I. Hummels in 1976 listed Hum. 395 as an Open Number meaning that there had been no design assigned to this number, but one might be assigned later. Research by this author unearthed different facts. A figurine described as "A little boy with a lamb by a fence" had been registered in May 30, 1972. Later, a search by Robert Miller and the Goebel Company located the prototype designed in 1972 by Gerhard Skrobek. The name used in German for this figurine is *Hirtenbub* which means "Young Shepherd." The original drawing of this motif by Sister Hummel has not been found, nor have any graphics been located.

395 Shepherd Boy *(Assigned). Artist's concept.*

396 Ride into Christmas

Indicator	Size	Status	TMK-1	TMK-2	TMK-3	TMK-4	TMK-5	TMK-6
396/2/0	?	P	—	—	—	—	—	95
396	5¾"	P	—	—	—	400	225	175

Sister Hummel's original drawing of this motif was adapted into a figurine in 1970 by Gerhard Skrobek, according to Goebel Company records. It was registered in the U.S. Copyright Office on December 3, 1971. The U.S. catalogs of 1972 only list the larger size, Hum. 396, incised 1971. The smaller size was not made available until the latter part of 1982 at $95. This will bring an example within reach of the many collectors who would like to own one. It will also be more adaptable to displaying in a shadow box with the 1972 Annual Plate, Hum. 268, which used this design. While the larger piece is available in TMK-4, 5, and 6, the TMK-4 mark is very scarce and commands varying premiums. The German name of this piece is *Fahrt in die Weihnacht,* which translates about the same as the English name. The original drawing is owned by Ars Edition and has been published in graphic form as H 316. The Hummel calendar for December 1976 has a picture of this figurine that makes another interesting companion piece for display.

396 Ride into Christmas, *copyright 1971, TMK-5.*

399 **Valentine Joy**, *Goebel Collectors' Club Limited Edition. Dous Collection.*

397-398 Open Numbers

Indicator	Size	Status	TMK-1	TMK-2	TMK-3	TMK-4	TMK-5	TMK-6
397-398		O						

According to the information available from the Goebel Company, these two numbers have not been assigned to any Hummel design, and therefore they are being listed as ones which are open and may or may not be assigned to a new product adapted from one of Sister Hummel's drawings. The last search of the U.S. copyrights did not produce any subject registered with these numbers.

399 Valentine Joy

Indicator	Size	Status	TMK-1	TMK-2	TMK-3	TMK-4	TMK-5	TMK-6
399	5¼"	D	—	—	—	—	?	95

In 1980, this number and name was used for a fourth special Limited Edition sold only to members of the Goebel Collectors' Club. The piece could be purchased when members presented the redemption card issued to them with their 1980 membership card (sometime between June 1, 1980 and May 31, 1981). The German inscription on the heart of Valentine Joy is *I mag di*, meaning "I Like You" compared to "I Love You Very Much" for Hum. 387. The original drawing by Sister Hummel is owned by Ars Edition, who produced an exact replica of it as H 335.

399 **Valentine Joy** *base showing TMK-6 and artist year-date.*

400-499

No record of assigned designs could be found for this number series until the fall of 1981 when Goebel introduced six new figurines in the Hummel line. Included in the group were Hum. 414, In Tune; Hum. 415, Thoughtful; and Hum. 421, It's Cold, the first M. I. Hummel's in the 400 series.

414 In Tune

Indicator	Size	Status	TMK-1	TMK-2	TMK-3	TMK-4	TMK-5	TMK-6
414	4"	P	—	—	—	—	—	115

The melodic pair featured in bas-relief on the fourth Annual Bell, Hum. 703, In Tune, can now be purchased as a matching figurine.

414 **In Tune** *issued 1981, TMK-6. Courtesy Goebel Collectors' Club.*

415 Thoughtful

Indicator	Size	Status	TMK-1	TMK-2	TMK-3	TMK-4	TMK-5	TMK-6
415	4½"	P	—	—	—	—	—	105

This small scholar with large book is the companion piece to the third Annual Bell, Hum. 702, also named Thoughtful. (See for more history.)

415 **Thoughtful,** *issued 1981, TMK-6. Courtesy Goebel Collectors' Club.*

421 It's Cold

Indicator	Size	Status	TMK-1	TMK-2	TMK-3	TMK-4	TMK-5	TMK-6
421	4½"	P	—	—	—	—	—	80

The newest Limited Edition produced for members of the Goebel Collectors' Club, Hum. 421, It's Cold, may be obtained by presenting a 1982-1983 redemption card and $80 to an authorized dealer.

500-599

Rumors of an Annual Hummel Mother's Day Plate have not become an actuality, but an indication of serious consideration is evidenced by a copyright for Hum. 500 on January 1, 1975, GF1152, with a tentative description of a Mother's Day plate, "Flowers for Mother."

421 **It's Cold,** *Limited Edition for Goebel Collectors' Club. Courtesy Goebel Collectors' Club.*

690 Smiling Through, Plaque

Indicator	Size	Status	TMK-1	TMK-2	TMK-3	TMK-4	TMK-5	TMK-6
690	5¾"	D	—	—	—	—	50	—

This circular, bas-relief plaque, 5¾" in diameter, is based on an original drawing of Sister Hummel's which is owned by Ars Edition. It has been published as graphic H 354 from the original. This plaque was selected for the second Limited Edition exclusively for members of the Goebel Collectors' Club in 1978. It is labeled as follows: "Exclusive Special Edition No. 2, Hum. 690 for members of the Goebel Collectors' Club."

690 **Smiling Through,** *Plaque, Limited Edition, Goebel Collectors' Club, 1978-1979, TMK-5. Courtesy Goebel Collectors' Club.*

700 Let's Sing, *First Annual Hummel Bell, 1978, TMK-5. Courtesy Goebel Collectors' Club.*

700   Annual Bell, Let's Sing, 1978

Indicator	Size	Status	TMK-1	TMK-2	TMK-3	TMK-4	TMK-5	TMK-6
700	6″	D	—	—	—	—	50	—

The first issue of a series of annual bells about 6″ high was exciting news. The motif was in bas-relief (see Hum. 110 for more information). On the reverse side, 1978 is embossed and highlighted in red. The reception of this piece, issued at a list price of $50, was phenomenal. By June of 1978, sales in the secondary market at $300 were not uncommon. Some Hummel collectors were upset because they could not buy either the plate or bell for 1978. The bell contains a blue transfer label overglaze with the following inside: "First Edition, Annual Bell, Hum. 700, Handcrafted." It also had the TMK-5 mark, with W. Germany, and 1977 as the copyright year.

701 Farewell, *Second Annual Hummel Bell, 1979, TMK-5. Courtesy Goebel Collectors' Club.*

701   Annual Bell, Farewell, 1979

Indicator	Size	Status	TMK-1	TMK-2	TMK-3	TMK-4	TMK-5	TMK-6
701	6¼″	D	—	—	—	—	70	—

The bas-relief is the same motif used for the figurine of the same name, Hum. 65, which should be referred to for background. The inscriptions on this Second Annual Bell and the red embossed year, 1979, follow the same pattern as described before for the first issue, Hum. 700. By 1980 this bell could be obtained on the secondary market for considerably less than issue price.

702 Thoughtful, *Third Annual Hummel Bell, 1980, TMK-6. Courtesy Goebel Collectors' Club.*

702   Annual Bell, Thoughtful, 1980

Indicator	Size	Status	TMK-1	TMK-2	TMK-3	TMK-4	TMK-5	TMK-6
702	6¼″	D	—	—	—	—	—	85

This third bell issue has Hum. 415 as a matching figurine. It is obviously closely related to Hum. 14 A. This 1980 bell was issued at a list price of $85. The bas-relief was adapted from Sister Hummel's drawing, which has been published as graphic H 196 by Ars Edition.

703 Annual Bell, In Tune, 1981

Indicator	Size	Status	TMK-1	TMK-2	TMK-3	TMK-4	TMK-5	TMK-6
703	6¼"	D	—	—	—	—	—	85

The subject of the fourth Annual Bell, In Tune, was adapted from Sister Hummel's original drawing which was published by Ars Edition as graphic H 144. A matching figurine was made available, Hum. 414, In Tune, in 1981 for $115.

703 In Tune, *Fourth Annual Hummel Bell, 1981, TMK-6. Courtesy Goebel Collectors' Club.*

704 Annual Bell, She Loves Me, 1982

Indicator	Size	Status	TMK-1	TMK-2	TMK-3	TMK-4	TMK-5	TMK-6
704	6¼"	P	—	—	—	—	—	85

To date, no original drawing of Sister Hummel's has been identified that matches this motif. (See Hum. 174 for figurine of same name.)

704 She Loves Me, *Fifth Annual Hummel Bell, 1982, TMK-6. Courtesy Dorothy Dous.*

705 Annual Bell, Knit One, 1983

Indicator	Size	Status	TMK-1	TMK-2	TMK-3	TMK-4	TMK-5	TMK-6
705	6¼"	P	—	—	—	—	—	?

The motif features one of Sister Hummel's busy little knitters. Original drawing for this design is not known at this time.

705 Knit One, *Sixth Annual Hummel Bell, 1983, TMK-6. Courtesy Goebel Collectors' Club.*

(L to R) *Czech, 842; Czech, 841. Both copyrighted 1940, courtesy W. Goebel Co.*

800-999 International M. I. Hummel Figurines

A sharp-eyed "picker" in a Budapest flea market in 1976 realized some unusual looking figurines in folk costumes were M. I. Hummel figurines. The chance to make a small, quick profit was the motivation for gambling on them for quick resale to a dealer in Austria. Rumors of this reached the U.S. It took the positive persistence of a full-blooded collector-detective, Robert L. Miller, to convert rumor into fact. Having finally acquired eight figurines in Eastern European costumes, all signed 𝔐.𝒥.Hummel , he obtained the permission of the Goebel Company to search their archives. This resulted in more figurines which are illustrated here. The international figurines project was abandoned when World War II began. Some international models, such as Hum. 947, "Goose Girl," have easily recognized counterparts (Hum. 47, Goose Girl). Are there more of these extremely rare examples to be found? The answer is yes. Several duplicates of these have surfaced and are valued in the five-digit figures.

Serbian figurine, 812, copyrighted 1940, courtesy W. Goebel Co.

(L to R) *Slav, 831; Slav, 832; Slav, 833. All copyrighted 1940, courtesy W. Goebel Co.*

(L to R) *Bulgarian, 810; Bulgarian, 809; Bulgarian, 810; Bulgarian, Bulgarian, 806. All copyrighted 1940, courtesy W. Goebel Co.*

(L) *Base of Bulgarian figurine, 808, showing Incised Crown, stamped Full Bee TMK-2, and incised Germany. (R) Base of Bulgarian, 806, with Bulgarian identification at top and bottom.*

(L to R) *Hungarian, 852; Hungarian, 853; Hungarian, 852. All copyrighted 1940, courtesy W. Goebel Co.*

1000-2000 M.I. Hummel Dolls

On January 3, 1953, Hum. 1809, "Peterle"; Hum. 1810, "Rosl"; Hum. 1811, "Mirel"; and Hum. 1812, "Franel" were registered in the U.S. Copyright Office. The names of Hum. 1802 and 1803 listed on February 2, 1967, recorded as GF440 and GF450 in the U.S. Copyright Office, were "Boy with Wicker Basket on Back" and "Girl with Broom." They are molded of plastic.

Non M. I. Hummel Items
Sister M.I. Hummel Busts

HU-1 M. I. Hummel Bust, *old style, incised "Hu-1, 1965," approximately 15" high, TMK-4.*

Indicator	Size	Status	TMK-1	TMK-2	TMK-3	TMK-4	TMK-5	TMK-6
HU-1	15"	D	—	—	—	800	—	—
HU-2(w)	5"	D	—	—	—	50	40	—
HU-2(c)	5"	D	—	—	—	—	75	—

While these three items are included here, they are not the result of a work of art by Sister Hummel herself, but rather the work of Goebel's master modeler, Gerhard Skrobek, who created HU-1 in 1965. The large, 15" bust in white bisque carries TMK-4. Smaller, white bisque bust, HU-2(w) was sculpted in 1967. M.J.Hummel is incised on front of base, with Skrobek on the back. Underside is incised with model number plus blue TMK-5 transfer label. Original list price: $15. The same bust in lifelike color, HU-2(c), was offered as a Limited Edition available only to third-year members of the Goebel Collectors' Club. Issue price in 1979-1980 was $75.

Top:

(L to R) *Bulgarian. 808; Bulgarian, 811; Swedish, 824; Swedish, 825; Swedish, 825. All copyrighted 1940, courtesy W. Goebel Co.*

Bottom:

(L to R) *Serbian, 812; Serbian, 968; Serbian, 813; Serbian, 904; Serbian, 947. All copyrighted 1940, courtesy W. Goebel Co.*

Selection of twenty folded Hummel notecards with envelopes, boxed — $15.

Ars Edition Hummel Collection

Sister Hummel's art was well known in graphic form before it was adapted to figurines by the Goebel Company. Ars Sacra, Joseph Müller Verlag, a religious publishing house, obtained their first Hummel drawings from the Franciscan Convent in Siessen in March of 1933, while Berta was still a novice. These were so well received by both publisher and public that she was hard pressed to meet Müller's commissions and the public's demand for more subjects. They were first distributed as postcards, notepaper, and prints all lithographed directly from the original drawings. In fact, the first M.J.Hummel figurines were sculpted in 1935 by Arthur Möller using Ars Sacra postcards as models.

In 1935 Sister Hummel returned to the academy in Munich for further study. The academy was located only a short distance from Ars Sacra, and a close relationship developed between Berta, Joseph Müller, and his wife Maximiliane. Ideas for new subjects were suggested by the couple. Mrs. Müller was adept at naming the drawings. In 1939 Ars Sacra published their first Hummel book, *Hui, Die Hummel,* of approximately seventy examples of her work in full color accompanied by related short verses. Because of the Nazi fanaticism about religion this book was suppressed. At that time the publisher Müller only received sufficient allocation of paper for export demands to obtain sorely needed foreign exchange. The book was later translated into English and published in 1972 as *The Hummel.* The hardbound copy is still in print at $15.

Hardbound edition of The Hummel *book featuring sixty-eight* Hummel *drawings in full color and light verse — $15.*

Hardwood musical jewelry boxes lined in red velvet are offered in two sizes. Single compartment — $30. Double compartment — $50.

Famous Hummel pair, Apple Tree Girl and Boy oval trays — $5.95, each

(L) *Postcard calendar — $4.95.* (R) *Ars Edition 1983 Hummel calendar — $9.95.*

Today in the U.S. the application of replicas of Hummel drawings has been expanded into many new forms of decorative art by Joseph Müller's great-grandson, Jacques Nauer, President of Ars Edition, Inc., of Seaford, New York, who continues the Hummel tradition his family founded fifty years ago. These art forms are illustrated and described on the pages following.

The once universally popular postcards are no longer published. Some have become collectors' items and are sold in the secondary market at prices ranging from fifty cents to two dollars, depending on subject and condition. These single postcards have been superseded by an assortment of popular Hummel designs on folded note cards with envelopes. A new, boxed assortment of twenty different Hummel subjects sells for $15 currently. There is also an eighteen notecard assortment expecially for the Christmas season featuring appropriate drawings such as "Ride into Christmas." The boxed set, imprinted with "Greetings and Best Wishes/for a Merry Christmas and a Happy New Year," is priced at $9.

Created especially for Hummel collectors, but also destined to appeal to several million Christmas ornament collectors, is Ars Edition's First Annual Christmas ornament introduced in 1982. The unbreakable, 3¼" gold satin wrapped ball is decorated with a frieze created from three Hummel Nativity prints: H 624, Gift Bearers; H 625, Angel's Music; and H 626, A Gift for Jesus. This appealing collectible is attractively boxed and priced at $6.

The first postcard calendars were published in 1946; present size is 4⅛" x 9⅛". Uniquely, this calendar is printed on card stock, and the illustrations can be easily removed for subsequent use as postcards. Price of the 1983 version is $4.95. Prices for older issues found in the secondary market may well be higher for scarce years. A second, large sized calendar has been produced since 1976 with different designs in each issue. In 1983 this large, 11¾" x 16½" size, titled "The Professions," will sell for $9.95. It is quite likely that the new issues will become desirable collectibles just as the older ones have. Some collectors have written that they enjoy the

First annual Christmas ornament from Ars Edition, satin, 3¼" diameter — $6.

Authematic Hummel jigsaw puzzles, 500 pieces, 16" x 20" — $8, each.

Wooden framed, pullcord musical wallpictures with ribbon hangers in choice of six motifs — $14.50, each.

Hummel graphic versions more than the figurines.

Many readers say that they are deeply moved by Hummel Art, but some forms are beyond their means. Ars Edition, Inc., has successfully solved that problem for the young collector and those operating on a tight budget. Instead of buying a hundred-dollar figurine, the beginner could start with one or more professionally matted prints of well-known Hummel subjects. These shrink-wrapped prints are 13" x 16", overall, and can be purchased for $6, ready to be hung on the wall or framed under glass. A smaller, 7½" x 9" matted size, is offered in thirty-six tempting motifs at $3, each. An interesting "picture wall" could be made for under one-hundred dollars. Good decorative accompaniments to the matted prints are the wallplaques which are offered in five matched pairs such as "Mother's Helper" and "Little Bookkeeper." Charming wallplaques, featuring Hummel graphics mounted on stained wooden backgrounds have gold colored hangers and sell for $6.50, each.

New from Ars Edition are the 16" x 20" boxed jigsaw puzzles consisting of over five-hundred interlocking pieces and priced at $8, each. At present "Ring Around the Rosie" and "Adventure Bound" are two of four subjects available in boxes decorated by pictures of the original drawings. The covers themselves offer interesting decorative possibilities.

Fine graphic Hummel ˙ Art is not limited to paper surfaces as proved by Ars Edition's new pair of 12" x 16" oval metal trays decorated with the much beloved Hummel "Apple Tree Boy" (H 297) and "Apple Tree Girl" (H 298). These richly lithographed designs are scratch- and water-resistant and equipped with hangers so they can be used either for decorative or functional purposes. The price of each is $5.95.

Probably the most popular items appealing to millions of limited edition collectors are Ars Edition's set of twelve 5" silver-plated spoons, each with a different Hummel design inset in the top of the spoon. The second edition has now been issued and will be offered until the end of 1983. These editions are stamped on the back with the Hummel signature, Ars Edition, the copyright year, and silver plated. Some of the first editions may be still available in some locations or possibly in the secondary market. They sold for $13 each, as does the second edition which is now being distributed. These spoons are of special interest to three groups: Hummel collectors, souvenir spoon collectors, and limited edition collectors.

Other silver-plated limited edition items in Hummel designs are the annual Christmas spoons and bells. The first edition bell was issued in 1981 with "Christmas Angel" (H 431) as the design. This was followed by "Guiding Angel" (H 438) in 1982, then "Prayer of Adoration" (H 434) for 1983. The 1984 Christmas spoon will have "Heavenly Duo" (H 446) as the motif. These sell for $13 each and are limited to the year dated on the bowl of the spoon. After issue, the die is destroyed. The first annual bell arrived a year later in 1982 with Hummel "Sunny Weather" (H 287) as the inset design at the top. The 1983 motif is "Ring Around the Rosie" (H 204), and the following two years will be "Telling Her Secret" (H 291) 1984, and "Quartet" (H 284) for 1985. Currently these annual bells sell for $19.50 each and are of interest to bell collectors as well as Hummel Art collectors. Mother's Day spoons also were first issued in 1982 and likewise will be continued with a new design each year. These 5" spoons also sell for $13.

A natural combination of Hummel Art and German craftsmanship by Ars Edition is found in their models of famous Black Forest clocks with key wound, thirty-hour movements. Available with a choice of six Hummel graphics, the clocks have dropped pendulums and weight chains. The selling price is $15.

Limited edition silverplated collectors' spoons feature twelve different examples of
~~Hummel~~ *Art — $13, each.*

An excellent child's gift is any one of six different Hummel designs on musical wallpictures, each with a melody appropriate to the scene. These circular wooden framed pictures feature Swiss music box movements operated by a pullcord. They sell for $14.50, at present.

Reserved for the top of the line are some fine examples of European cabinetry and finish in the form of single and double compartment musical jewelry boxes elegantly lined in red velvet. The single compartment boxes are decoupaged in a selection of four Hummel drawings. Double compartment boxes are offered in a choice of two different paired drawings. The double compartment is 8¼" x 6" and priced at $50. The single is 4¼" x 6" and is priced at $30.

Other Hummel collectibles currently available from Ars Edition include Advent calendars at $2.95, each; pendants for $10, each; and a large selection of purse-sized mirrors, each featuring a different Hummel print and priced at $2.

Expect a continuation of the limited edition series now produced, plus the introduction of many other attractive and useful Hummel Art collectibles derived from the Ars Edition collection of more than three-hundred original Hummel drawings.

Black Forest pendulum clocks from Ars Edition are available with choice of six different Hummel drawings. Key wind movement — $15, each.

"Sunny Weather" pendant on handsome, 24" rope chain — $10.

Mother's Day, 1982 limited edition spoon — $13.

(L) *"Guiding Angel" 1982 Christmas bell.* **(R)** *"Ring Around the Rosie" 1983 annual bell — $19.50, each.*

"Guiding Angel" 1982 Christmas spoon — $13.

Alphabetical Guide to Model Numbers

NAME	MODEL	CLASS
A FAIR MEASURE	345	F
ACCORDION BOY	185	F
ADORATION	23	F
ADORATION W/BIRD	105	F
Advent Grp. w/Candle	31	CAN
Advent Candlesticks (3)	115-6-7	CAN
ADVENTURE BOUND	347	F
Angel Cloud	206	HWF
Angel Duet	193	CAN
ANGEL DUET	261	F
Angel Duet	146	HWF
Angel, Guardian	29	HWF
Angel, Joy. News w/Trpt.	242	HWF
Angel, Joy. News w/Lute	241	HWF
Angel, Joy. News w/Lute	38	CAN
Angel, Joy. News w/Acdn.	39	CAN
Angel, Joy. News w/Trpt.	40	CAN
Angel Lights	241	CAN
Angel Prayer (Left, right)	91 A&B	HWF
ANGEL SERENADE	83	F
ANGEL SERENADE (Klng.)	214/D	F
ANGEL SERENADE (Klng.)	260 E	F
Angel Shrine (Devotion)	147	HWF
Angel with Bird (Left)	167	HWF
Angel with Birds (Right)	22	HWF
Angel with Cross	354 C	HWF
Angel with Flowers (child)	36	HWF
Angel with Lantern	354 A	HWF
Angel with Trumpet	354 B	HWF
Angel Trio (A) (Sitting)	38, 39, 40	CAN
ANGEL TRIO (B)	238 A B C	F
ANGEL, TUNEFUL	359	F
Angelic Prayer	75	HWF
Angelic Sleep w/Candle	25	CAN
ANGELIC SONG	144	F
Anniversary Plates —		
1975-80	280-81	PLT
Annual Bells — 1978-83	700-05	BL
Annual Plates — 1971-86	264-279	PLT
APPLE TREE BOY	142	F
APPLE TREE GIRL	141	F
Apple Tree Boy	230	TLP
Apple Tree Girl	229	TLP
Apple Tree Boy & Girl	252 A&B	BE
ARITHMETIC LESSON	303	F
ART CRITIC	318	F
AT THE FENCE	324	F
AUF WIEDERSEHEN	153	F
AUTUMN HARVEST	355	F
Ba-Bee Rings (2)	30 A&B	PLQ
BAKER	128	F
BAKING DAY	330	F
BAND LEADER	129	F
BARNYARD HERO	195	F
BASHFUL	377	F
BE PATIENT	197	F
BEGGING HIS SHARE	9	F
BEHAVE	339	F
Being Punished	326	PLQ
BIG HOUSECLEANING	363	F
BIRD DUET	169	F
BIRD WATCHER	300	F
BIRTHDAY CAKE	338	F
BIRTHDAY PRESENT	341	F
BIRTHDAY SERENADE	218	F
Birthday Serenade	231	TLP
Birthday Serenade	234	TLP
BLESSED EVENT	333	F
BOOKWORM	3	F
BOOKWORM	8	F
Bookworms (Boy & Girl)	14	BE
BOOTS	143	F
BOY W/ACCORDION	390	F
Boy w/Bird	166	AT
BOY W/HORSE	239 C	F
Boy w/Horse	117	CAN
BOY W/TOOTHACHE	217	F
BROTHER	95	F
BUILDER	305	F
BUSY STUDENT	367	F
Butterfly & Boy	139	PLQ
Candlelight	192	CAN
CARNIVAL	328	F
CELESTIAL MUSICIAN	188	F
CHEF, HELLO	124	F
CHICK GIRL	57	F
Chick Girl	III/57	CBX
Chick Girl & Playmates	61 B&A	BE
CHICKEN LICKEN	385	F
Child in Bed	137	PLQ
Child Jesus	26	HWF
CHILDREN TRIO (A)	239 A B C	F
CHILDREN TRIO (B)	389,390,391	F
CHIMNEY SWEEP	12	F
CHRIST CHILD	18	F
CHRISTMAS ANGEL	301	F
Christmas Angels (3)	115-6-7	CND
CHRISTMAS SONG	343	F
CINDERELLA	337	F
CLOSE HARMONY	336	F
COMPANIONS	370	F
CONCENTRATION	302	F
CONFIDENTIALLY	314	F
CONGRATULATIONS	17	F
COQUETTES	179	F
Cross with Doves	77	HWF
CROSSROADS	331	F
CULPRITS	56/A	F
Culprits	44 A	TLP
DADDY'S GIRLS	371	F
Dealer's Plaque	187 C	PLQ
DOCTOR	127	F
DOLL BATH	319	F
DOLL MOTHER	67	F
Doll Mother & Prayer B.B.	76	BE
Donkey	214/J & 260/L	NAT
DON'T BE SHY	379	F
Dove (Holy Spirit)	393	HWF
DUET	130	F
EASTER GREETINGS	378	F
EASTER TIME	384	F
EVENTIDE *Mar*	99	F
Eventide/Adoration	90 A&B	BE
FAREWELL	65	F
Farewell	103	TLP
FARM BOY	66	F
Farm Boy & Goose Girl	60 A&B	BE
FAVORITE PET	361	F
FEATHERED FRIENDS	344	F
FEEDING TIME	199	F
FESTIVAL HAR. W/MAN.	172	F
FESTIVAL HAR. W/FL.	173	F
Flitting Butterfly	139	PLQ
Flower Madonna	10	MAD
FLOWER VENDOR	381	F
FLYING ANGEL	366	F
FOLLOW THE LEADER	369	F
FOREST SHRINE	183	F
FOR FATHER	87	F
FOR MOTHER	257	F
FRIENDS	136	F
GAY ADVENTURE *Mars*	356	F
Girl w/Fir Tree	116	CAN
GIRL W/FROG	219	F
GIRL W/DOLL	239 B	F
GIRL W/NOSEGAY	239 A	F
Girl w/Nosegay	115	CAN
GIRL W/SHEET MUSIC	389	F
GIRL W/TRUMPET	391	F
GLOBE TROTTER	79	F
GOING HOME	383	F
GOING TO GRANDMA'S	52	F
GOOD FRIENDS	182	F
Good Friends	228	TLP
Good Friends & S.L.M.	251 A&B	BE
GOOD HUNTING	307	F
GOOD NIGHT	214 C	F
Good Night	260 D	NAT
GOOD SHEPHERD	42	F
Good Shepherd	35	HWF
GOOSE GIRL	47	F
Goose Girl & Farm Boy	60 A&B	BE
GROUP OF CHILDREN	392	F
Guardian Angel	29	HWF
Guardian Angel	248	HW F
GUARDIAN, LITTLE	145	F
GUIDING ANGEL	357	F
HAPPINESS	86	F
HAPPY BIRTHDAY	176	F
Happy Bugler	180	PLQ
HAPPY DAYS	150	F
Happy Days	232,235	TLP
HAPPY PASTIME	69	F
Happy Pastime	111/69	CBX
Happy Pastime	221	CBX
Happy Pastime	62	AT
HAPPY TRAVELLER	109	F
HEAR YE, HEAR YE	15	F
HEAVENLY ANGEL	21	F
Heavenly Angel	207	HWF
HEAVENLY LULLABY	262	F
HEAVENLY PROTECTION	88	F
Heavenly Song	113	CAN
HELLO	124	F
HELPING MOTHER	325	F
Herald Angels	37	CAN
Holy Family	246	HWF
Holy Family (Set)	214	NAT
HOME FROM MARKET	198	F
HOMEWARD BOUND	334	F
HONEY LOVER	312	F
Hum. Display Plqs.,	187-209	PLQ
"Hummel" Bust	HU-1&2	MIS
"Hummel" Bust	HU-1&2	MIS
I FORGOT	362	F
IN TUNE	414	F
INFANT JESUS	214/A	F
Infant Jesus	260 C	NAT
INFANT OF KRUMBAD	78	F
IT'S COLD	421	F
JOYFUL	53	F
Joyful	111/53	CBX
Joyful	33	AT
Joyful & Let's Sing	120	BE
Joyous News	27	CAN
Joyous News w/Lute	38	CAN

ABBREVIATIONS: AT-Ashtray; BE-Bookends; BL-Bell; CAN-Candleholders; CBX-Candybox; F-Figurine; HWF-Holy Water Font

NAME	MODEL	CLASS	NAME	MODEL	CLASS	NAME	MODEL	CLASS
Joyous News w/Accdn.	39	CAN	Merry Christmas	323	PLQ	SKIER	59	F
Joyous News w/Trmpt.	40	CAN	MERRY WANDERER	7&11	F	SMART LITTLE SISTER	346	F
JUST FISHING	373	F	Merry Wanderer	92,106	PLQ	Smiling Through	690	PLQ
JUST RESTING	112	F	Merry Wanderer	263	PLQ	SOLDIER BOY	332	F
Just Resting	11/112	TLP	"M.I. Hummel" Plaque	187	PLQ	SOLOIST	135	F
Just Resting	225	TLP	"M.I. Hummel" Plaques	205 +	PLQ	SPRING CHEER	72	F
King (Standing)	214/L	NAT	MISCHIEF MAKER	342	F	SPRING DANCE	353	F
King (Knlg. on one knee)	214/M	NAT	Moorish King	260N	NAT	Standing Boy	168	PLQ
King (Knlg. on two knees)	214/N	NAT	MORNING STROLL	375	F	STAR GAZER	132	F
King (Standing)	260 O	NAT	MOTHER'S DARLING	175	F	STITCH IN TIME	255	F
King (Kneeling)	260 P	NAT	MOTHER'S HELPER	133	F	Store Plaque	187 C	PLQ
KISS ME	311	F	MOUNTAINEER	315	F	STORMY WEATHER	71	F
Kneeling Angel	248	HWF	Nativity Set (Small)	214	NAT	STREET SINGER	131	F
KNITTING LESSON	256	F	Nativity Set (Large)	260	NAT	STROLLING ALONG	5	F
Lamb	214/O	NAT	NOT FOR YOU	317	F	SUNNY MORNING	313	F
LATEST NEWS	184	F	OFF TO SCHOOL	329	F	SURPRISE	94	F
LET'S SING	110	F	ON HOLIDAY	350	F	Swaying Lullaby	165	PLQ
Let's Sing	114	AT	ON SECRET PATH	386	F	SWEET GREETINGS	352	F
Let's Sing	111/110	CBX	OUT OF DANGER	56/B	F	SWEET MUSIC	186	F
LETTER TO SANTA	340	F	Out of Danger	44 B	TLP	TELLING HER SECRET	196	F
LITTLE BAND	392	F	Ox	214/K & 260/M	NAT	TENDERNESS	300	F
Little Band	388	CAN	PHOTOGRAPHER	178	F	THE ARTIST	304	F
Little Band w/Cndl.	288/M	MBX	PLAYMATES	58	F	THE BOTANIST	351	F
Little Band w/o Cndl.	392/M	MBX	Playmates & Chick Girl	61 A/B	BE	THE BUILDER	305	F
LITTLE BOOKKEEPER	306	F	Playmates	111/58	CBX	THE FLORIST	349	F
LITTLE CELLIST	89	F	POSTMAN	119	F	THE HOLY CHILD	70	F
LITTLE DRUMMER	240	F	PRAYER BEFORE BATTLE	20	F	THE MAIL IS HERE	226	F
LITTLE FIDDLER	2	F	PUPPY LOVE Nat	1	F	THE PROFESSOR	320	F
LITTLE FIDDLER	4	F	Puppy Love & Serenade	122	BE	THE RUNAWAY	327	F
Little Fiddler	93	PLQ	Quartet	134	PLQ	THOUGHTFUL	415	F
Little Fiddler	107	PLQ	RELAXATION	316	F	THRIFTY, LITTLE	118	F
LITTLE GABRIEL	32	F	RETREAT TO SAFETY	201	F	TIMID LITTLE SISTER	394	F
LITTLE GARDENER	74	F	Retreat to Safety	126	PLQ	Tiny Baby in Crib	138	PLQ
LITTLE GOAT HERDER	200	F	RIDE INTO CHRISTMAS	396	F	TO MARKET	49	F
Ltl. Goat Hrdr. & F'dng Time	250	BE	RING 'RND. T. ROSIE	348	F	To Market	101	TLP
LITTLE GUARDIAN	145	F	RUN-A-WAY, THE	327	F	To Market	223	TLP
LITTLE HELPER	73	F	ST. GEORGE	55	F	TRUMPET BOY	97	F
LITTLE HIKER	16	F	St. Joseph	214/B & 260/B	NAT	TUNEFUL ANGEL	359	F
LITTLE NURSE	376	F	SCHOOL BOY	82	F	Tuneful Goodnight	180	PLQ
LITTLE PHARMACIST	322	F	SCHOOL BOYS	170	F	UMBRELLA BOY	152 A	F
LITTLE SCHOLAR	80	F	SCHOOL GIRL	81	F	UMBRELLA GIRL	152 B	F
LITTLE SHOPPER	96	F	SCHOOL GIRLS	177	F	Vacation Time	125	PLQ
LITTLE SWEEPER	171	F	Searching Angel	310	PLQ	VALENTINE GIFT	387	F
LITTLE TAILOR	308	F	SENSITIVE HUNTER	6	F	VALENTINE JOY	399	F
LITTLE THRIFTY	118	F	SHEPHERD, GOOD	42	F	VILLAGE BOY	51	F
Little Tooter	214/H, 260/K	NAT	SERENADE	85	F	VISITING AN INVALID	382	F
LITTLE VELMA	219	F	Shepherd w/Sheep	214/F	NAT	VOLUNTEERS	50	F
LITTLEST ANGEL	365	F	SHEPHERD BOY	395	F	Volunteers	102	TLP
LOST SHEEP	68	F	Shepherd Boy	214/G	NAT	WAITER	154	F
LOST STOCKING	374	F	Shepherd Boy (Kneeling)	260 J	NAT	Wall Vases Boy & Girl	360/A B C	WVS
LUCKY BOY	335	F	Shepherd (Standing)	260 G	NAT	WASHDAY	321	F
Lullaby	24	CAN	Shepherd (Standing) w/Lamb	260 H	NAT	WATCHFUL ANGEL	194	F
LULLABY, HEAVENLY	262	F	Sheep (Lying)	260 R	NAT	WAYSIDE DEVOTION	28	F
LUTE SONG	368	F	SHE LOVES ME, S.L.M.N.	174	F	Wayside Devotion	104	TLP
Madonnas	214/A & 260/A	NAT	She Loves Me, She L.M.N.	227	F	WAYSIDE HARMONY	111	F
Madonna (Wire frame)	222	PLQ	She Loves Me & G. Fr'nds.	251 B/A	BE	Wayside Harmony & J. Rest'g	121	BE
Madonna w/Child	48	PLQ	SHEPHERD'S BOY	64	F	Wayside Harmony	224	TLP
Madonna w/Child	243	HWF	SHINING LIGHT	358	F	Wayside Harmony	II/111	TLP
Madonna, Flower	10	MAD	Shrine	100	TLP	WE CONGRATULATE	220	F
Madonna, Seated	151	MAD	SIGNS OF SPRING	203	F	We Congratulate	214/E & 260/F	NAT
Madonna w/Halo	45	MAD	Silent Night	54	CAN	WEARY WANDERER	204	F
Madonna w/o Halo	46	MAD	Silent Night w/Bl. Child	31	CAN	WHICH HAND?	258	F
MAIL IS HERE	226	F	SINGING LESSON	63	F	WHITSUNTIDE	163	F
Mail Is Here	140	PLQ	Singing Lesson	111/63	CBX	W/ LOVING GRTNGS.	309	F
MAN GOING TO MKT.	191	F	Singing Lesson	34	AT	WOMAN GOING TO Mkt.	190	F
MAN READING PAPER	181	F	Singing Lesson	272	PLT	WOMAN KNITTING	189	F
MARCH WINDS	43	F	SISTER	98	F	WORSHIP	84	F
MAX AND MORITZ	123	F	Sitting Angel (Angel w/Bird)	22	HWF	Worship	164	HWF
MEDITATION	13	F						

About the Author

For several years John F. Hotchkiss has been a resident Fellow at the Rochester (New York) Museum of Arts and Science Center as a result of his specialized knowledge of antiques, and especially glass, in which he has had an interest for over forty years.

During the last twenty years he has produced a number of books, such as *Art Glass Handbook, Carder's Steuben Glass, Cut Glass Handbook, Bottle Collector's Handbook, Hummel Art I,* and *Hummel Art II.* He also wrote *Limited Edition Collectibles,* the first comprehensive book on this subject.

After retiring as superintendent of an Eastman Kodak Company manufacturing division, he lectured on antiques and collectibles on three world cruises, at which time he became interested in the Hummel figurines he had been buying for his daughters. After three years of research, he wrote the first complete book on Hummel Art in 1978 and followed with *Supplements* in 1979 and 1980.

In addition, Mr. Hotchkiss appraises antiques and collections for insurance and estate purposes under the auspices of Hotchkiss Associates.

A native of Geneseo, New York, he is a graduate of Carnegie-Mellon University in Pittsburgh and a past president of their alumni federation. He and his wife, Fidelis, live in Sanibel, Florida, but spend the summer months in Rochester, New York.

— *Alice Walsh*

Place
Stamp
Here

Hummel Handbook
P.O. Box 1317
Des Moines, IA 50305

Place
Stamp
Here

Hummel Handbook
P.O. Box 1317
Des Moines, IA 50305

Please send the following information:

☐ How I can buy additional copies of this book.

☐ How I can buy *Hummel Art II* by John F. Hotchkiss. The most complete reference book on the subject.

☐ Free copy of "Hummel" Collectors' Club, Inc. — newsletter by Dorothy Dous.

☐ Name of the nearest Ars Edition, Inc., dealer.

☐ Information about the Goebel Collectors' Club.

☐ Notification of any new books on Hummel Art or Ars Edition, Inc., issues.

Name _____

Address _____

City _____ *State* _____ *Zip* _____

Please send the following information:

☐ How I can buy additional copies of this book.

☐ How I can buy *Hummel Art II* by John F. Hotchkiss. The most complete reference book on the subject.

☐ Free copy of "Hummel" Collectors' Club, Inc. — newsletter by Dorothy Dous.

☐ Name of the nearest Ars Edition, Inc., dealer.

☐ Information about the Goebel Collectors' Club.

☐ Notification of any new books on Hummel Art or Ars Edition, Inc., issues.

Name _____

Address _____

City _____ *State* _____ *Zip* _____